Sheinton
Shropshire

Geology, Landscape,
History and Archaeology

By
Norman Davies, Margaret Hill, Trevor Hill,
Chris Rayner, Mike Rayner, Dee Revell

Edited by Mike Rayner

Sheinton, Shropshire, *Geology, Landscape, History and Archaeology*
By: Norman Davies, Margaret Hill, Trevor Hill, Chris Rayner, Mike Rayner, Dee Revell
Editor: Mike Rayner
http://www.sheinton.org.uk

A catalogue record for this book is available from the British Library. This first edition, published in 2006

ISBN: 0-9545251-1-6

Further copies of this book can be obtained by contacting the Editor at 36 Severn Way, Cressage, Shrewsbury, Shropshire SY5 6DS

Typeset and designed by Naughty Mutt Limited
http://www.naughtymutt.com 01939 233 123
in Bembo 11.5pt on 13pt
Printing by Leiston Press, Leiston, Suffolk 01728 833 003

ACKNOWLEDGEMENTS

S o many people have helped in so many ways that we cannot mention them all here. But thanks to everyone for their direct and indirect support for the book and the Sheinton Heritage Project as a whole.

Peter and John Taylor of Sheinton Hall Farm
Martin and Rebecca Brassington of Belswardine
Maldwyn Davies of Church Farm
Staff of Shropshire Archives
Hugh Hannaford of the Shropshire Archaeology Service
Peter Reavill of the Portable Antiquities Scheme.

Most of the illustrations are the work/property of the contributors to the book. We are grateful to them. For permission to use other items we are indebted to:
Shropshire Archives (figs 5.3-4, 7.1, 7.3-4, 8.1, 8.3, 11.1, colour photo11.1)
Churchwardens of Sheinton Church (figs 7.7, 7.8, 9.1)
Mike Bassett of the National Museum of Wales (figs 2.7, 2.9)
David Pannett (figs 1.1, 1.2)
Shropshire County Museum Service (fig 2.10)
Hon H F C Vane (fig 5.2)
Peter and John Taylor (fig 5.5)
Amanda C Hill (fig 8.2)
Mrs Faith Davies (fig 8.4)
Wenlock Archives (fig 11.3)
Mr J McFall (fig 11.4)

THE SHEINTON HERITAGE GROUP

The Sheinton Heritage Group. Photo credit: Brian Revell

The group was formally constituted on 8th January 2004 for the benefit of the community of Sheinton and the surrounding area. Its objectives were: to explore the local heritage, its history, archaeology, geography, geology and ecology; to give opportunities for local people to take part in archaeological and geological activity and researching historical sources; to exhibit and disseminate the findings through lectures, workshops, guided walks and visits, and through a website (www.sheinton.org.uk) and book; to raise public awareness of the local heritage of Sheinton and the surrounding area and to involve all ages in the project.

The Group was funded by a grant from Local Heritage Inititiative for a two-year period finishing on 30th June 2006. We believe we have gone a long way towards achieving our objectives. And in the course of doing so there has been much learning, pleasure and comradeship.

FOREWORD

In this book we have set out to record some of our discoveries about the place called Sheinton. We have used various sources of information such as rocks and fossils, pieces of pottery and metal objects, buildings and written documents. However, we can only use those that have both survived the ravages of time and also been discovered. Such objects do not speak, so we cannot discuss with them how or why they were created in the first place. We found a Roman coin which can be dated by the profile of the Emperor Carinus to 283-285 but we cannot say who dropped it or in what circumstances it was lost. We can find detailed documents such as a *deed* which tells us about the transfer of a property. Yet without further information about the persons involved or the place that it refers to we may not be able to tell what led to its being drawn up in the first place. We can, however, use our expertise to explain what these artefacts tell us about Sheinton's past, interpreting our discoveries in the light of current scholarship, even though future researchers may uncover evidence that will amend or even totally overturn what we have written.

We hope that you, the reader, will find our book stimulating, interesting and helpful in understanding the development of the community of Sheinton.

8

CONTENTS

CHAPTER

1
SEVERN MEANDERINGS

Chris Rayner

When we gaze on the statue of the shapely goddess of the River Severn, Sabrina, in the Dingle in Shrewsbury, we are reminded that around us, in a big loop, flows Great Britain's longest river and one of Shropshire's distinctive landscape features. But it might not have been so! In late Tertiary times, the early (proto-) River Severn flowed from the Plynlimmon mass to Welshpool, then turned north to the present Dee estuary. It was the Quaternary Period of Ice Ages that left us the legacy of our much-loved River Severn.

How did this come about?

Some 20,000 years ago a glacier poured down what was the upper Severn valley from the ice-capped Welsh mountains. It converged near Shrewsbury with an even more powerful one coming from the Irish Sea. They became a vast ice-sheet which filled the plain and over-rode the higher ground of Wenlock Edge and much of what is now Telford, finally reaching its maximum extent south of Bridgnorth at Eardington.

As the climate began to improve, summer melting took place both at the edges and on the surface of the ice-sheet and melt-water poured down crevasses and ice caves emerging at the *snout* as a river. In this part of Shropshire, the encircling hills hindered movement at the base of the ice so that only the surface layers were able to move freely, sliding over the base. The basal layers were probably frozen to the ground underneath. Consequently the ice-sheet was stable enough to allow melt-water within the ice to cut a network of channels into the bedrock. Thus numerous sub-glacial channels were formed, some of which were being cut by water apparently flowing up-hill under the hydrostatic head provided by the thick ice cover above. Several such channels crossed the Wenlock watershed.

As the ice receded, melt-water was able to flow over the newly exposed land surface and most sub-glacial channels became choked up with sands and gravels. However, the channel near what is now Ironbridge was kept open as a greater volume of water flowed through, very powerfully cutting the channel deeper eventually to form the Ironbridge Gorge. As the edge of the ice-sheet had by this time receded north into the Shropshire Plain the new deepened valley was draining the area by gravity. The old headwaters of the Severn above Shrewsbury could not resume the former course to the Dee because of stagnant ice and glacial deposits blocking the outlet so the river continued in its new post-glacial channel, flowing past Cressage and Sheinton through the Ironbridge Gorge towards the Bristol channel. Thus today we enjoy the river, in winter flood or summer shallow, meandering past our villages (figure 1.1).

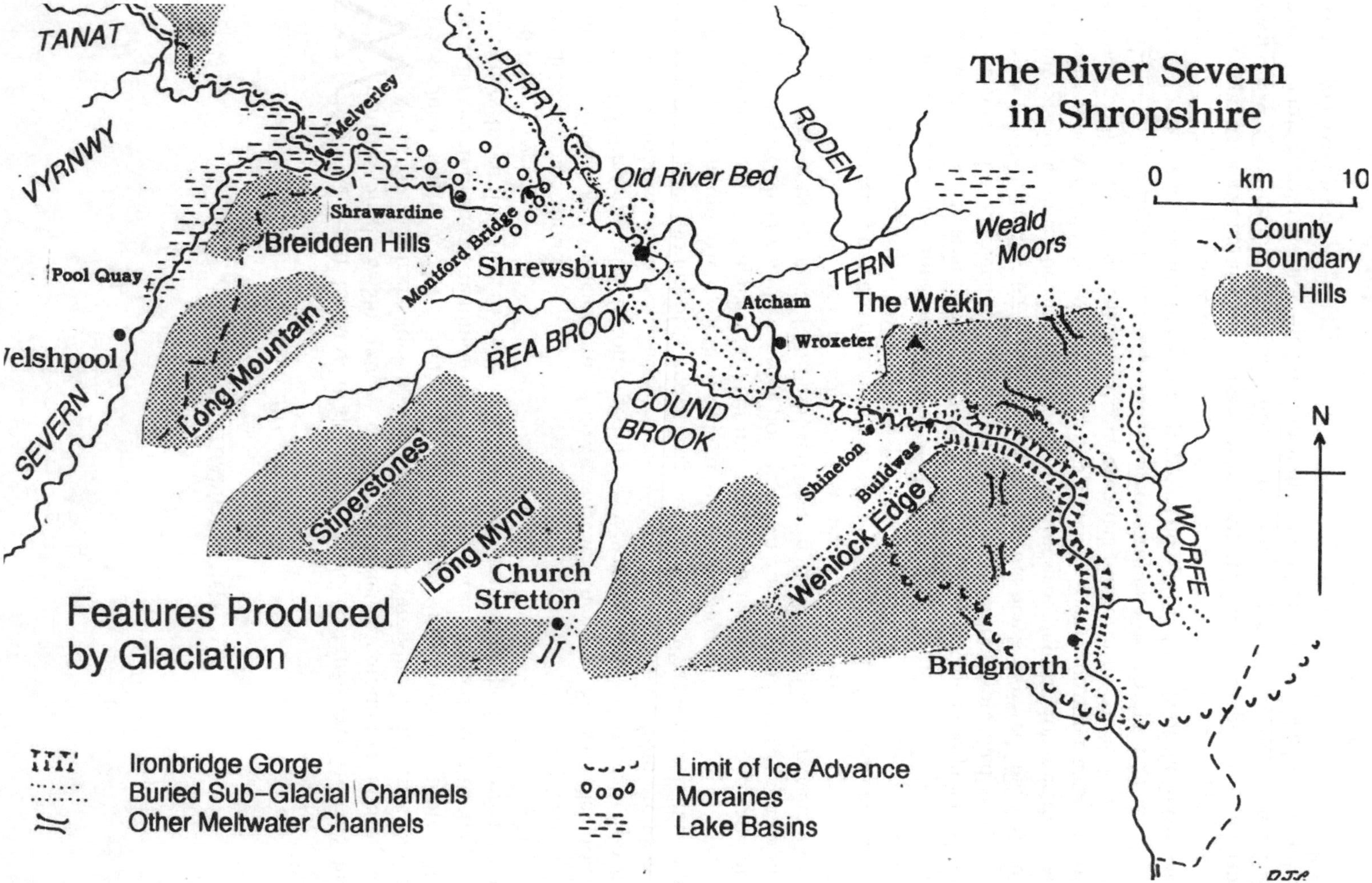

Figure 1.1 Glacial features along the Severn Valley (courtesy of David Pannett)

Lake Lapworth, true or false?

Controversy has reigned over the former existence of a huge lake named *Lapworth* by L J Wills in 1924, in honour of an eminent glaciologist of that name. Professor Wills was responsible for the Lake Lapworth theory that explained the formation of the Ironbridge Gorge by the overflowing of this enormous lake left by retreating ice and covering most of the North Shropshire Plain as far north as Wem, east to Newport and Gnosall and south to the Longmynd area and west to the Berwyns. For many years this was the accepted explanation but since the 1970s, new field research has cast doubt on its validity and several alternative theories have been put forward by J Shaw (1972), P Worsley (1975), R J O Hamblin (1986) and others. As yet there is no definitive explanation and the evidence is too complicated to describe here. However, recent research suggests an origin for the Ironbridge Gorge related to the sub-glacial channels mentioned earlier in combination with a series of smaller dammed-up lakes such as Lake Buildwas and masses of stagnant ice interspersed with outwash sands and gravels, rather than the neat, simple theory of overflowing Lake Lapworth down-cutting the gorge with its rushing waters.

Flood Plain, Meanders and Terraces

One of the most impressive views along the Severn valley is that looking across the river to Sheinton from a lay-by at Leighton. Here the river flows in a series of spectacular meanders over its flood plain, colour photo 1.1, (centre section).

It looks even more dramatic during floods when the whole flood plain becomes a sheet of water converging on the narrow neck of the Ironbridge Gorge. Between Cressage and Buildwas the erosional evidence, gravel banks, and scroll bars all point to gradual meander development and changing channel patterns as the bends migrate downstream. Through its geomorphological history, the river has occupied, at one time or another, most of the valley floor along this stretch, removing much of the glacial drift material that once filled the valley. So, along the Cressage-Sheinton-Buildwas section of the Severn, the flood-plain is clear of glacial deposits. They can be seen to best effect away from the flood plain in the form of sandy and gravelly mounds and ridges around Homer and Belswardyne then as heavy clayey till on Sheinwood Common. Perhaps the most striking and best-preserved glacial sands are those occurring at the former sand and gravel workings (now a landfill site) just downstream of Buildwas Abbey. There it is still possible to see thin cross-stratified units of Permo/Trias-derived red sands, considered the earliest fluvio-glacial deposits in the area, colour photo 1.2, (centre section).

For the last 10,000 years, since the ice finally melted, the Severn has been cutting down into its flood plain in a sporadic manner. In so doing it has left behind at successively higher levels than the present alluvium, flat river terraces composed of alluvium of earlier periods when the river was flowing at a higher level. The patchy remains of these can be seen either side of the river. There are at least 3 of these terraces but some researchers claim that more can possibly be identified. On the accompanying map the three terraces mapped by Pocock and others (1938) can be seen in descending order: Uffington, Cressage, and Atcham (figure 1.2).

Figure 1.2 Severn river terraces and floodplain from Cressage to Buildwas (courtesy of David Pannett)

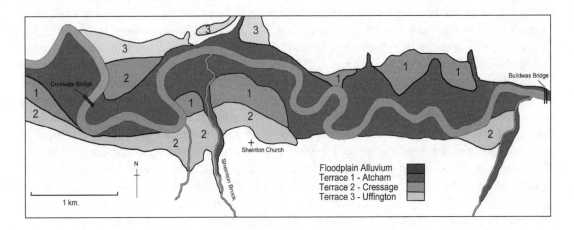

When we drive from Cressage to Sheinton we are on the Cressage Terrace and the drop down to the flood plain is clear to see. The terraces here can be correlated with those of tributaries and other river valleys to indicate sudden changes in rates of erosion. Occasionally the terrace alluvium has been found to contain animal bones which tell us something about the prevailing climate. These days alluvium deposition is slow but is visibly evident in times of flood.

It is only a few miles along the Severn from Cressage to Buildwas, a mere fraction of its total length but even in this short distance the landscape of its valley shaped by ice and water during the last 20,000 years reflects a varied erosional and depositional history. The more ancient underlying rocks in the area around Sheinton also have a fascinating story to tell as will be seen in the next chapter.

REFERENCES

Hamblin, R J O, The Pleistocene sequence of the Telford District, *Proceedings of Geological Association 97*, p986

Pannett, D, The physical background, in Morriss, R K, *The Shropshire Severn, 1994*

Pannett, D, Pulling the Plug on Lake Lapworth, in *Newsletter of Shropshire Geological Society,* April 2004

Pocock, R W, et al, *Shrewsbury District Geological Memoir*, 1938

Shaw, J, The Irish Sea glaciation of North Shropshire – some environmental reconstructions, *Field Studies 3,* no 4, 1972

Wills, L J, The development of the Severn Valley in the neighbourhood of Ironbridge & Bridgnorth, *Quarterly Journal of the Geological Society*, 80, 1924

Worsley, P, An Appraisal of the glacial Lake Lapworth concept in Phillips, A D M, &Turton, B J, (eds), *Environment, man and economic change*, 1975

2
SHEINTON ROCKS AND LANDSCAPE

Chris Rayner

Standing outside Sheinton church we see a gently rolling landscape with woods, fields and a scattering of farms and houses. The ground slopes down to the Sheinton brook, invisible from here but meandering to the River Severn a short distance away. To the left the land rises to Sheinwood Common and towards Wenlock Edge on the eastern boundary of the parish; to the right, beyond the brook, is Cressage parish with its plateau-like horizon. If we walk behind the church the Wrekin is just visible through winter trees and in between the ground drops quite abruptly down to the Severn. The landscape around us has been greatly changed by human activity but it was originally shaped by the underlying rocks and their immensely long history of repeated submergence, up-lift and erosion.

Sheinton Parish is underlain by six different rock types with a varied covering of fluvial and glacial superficial deposits, colour photo 2.1, (centre section).

The church stands on Kenley Grit, a hard pebbly sandstone, but this is capped by a layer of soft glacial sands and gravels. All around, the basal rock types are blanketed to a greater or lesser degree by glacial drift – sandy, clayey and varying in thickness.

On either side of the gritstone are soft Sheinton Shales to the west, and eastward, along the road to Much Wenlock, a series of mostly un-resistant shale with thin limestone layers, some very shelly, passing eventually into the well-known Wenlock Limestone which forms the Edge.

As one surveys the landscape from the churchyard with this knowledge in mind, it is surprising to see that *soft* rocks seem to form land higher than the Kenley Grit. Why? The answer seems to lie in the thick deposits of glacial till which plasters the underlying rocks. We shall now look more closely at Sheinton rocks, their characteristics, their environment of deposition and their importance today. Firstly it is helpful to know their age and relationship to one another. This can be seen by referring to the geological column *(figure 2.1, next page)*.

Sheinton Shales

The village of Sheinton (spelt 'Shineton' in Victorian times) gave its name to a formation of grey-blue shales, at least 800 metres thick. They dip, like the other sedimentary rocks in the parish, to the south-east and are known for their cone-in-cone structures and large, flattened rounded concretions which occur along bedding planes and often, after weathering, fall out into the stream bed. These have been called *stinkstones* because there is a distinct sulphurous smell if they are struck by a hammer. The photograph, colour photo 2.2 (centre section) shows concretions in situ. The Sheinton Shales, exposed in the brook of the same name, extend far beyond this parish into Cressage and across the River Severn to the southern flanks of the Wrekin. It was Calloway in 1877 who first distinguished the Sheinton Shales from the underlying Harnage Shales of the Caradoc Series of the Ordovician (not present in our parish). He was unable to demonstrate an unconformable

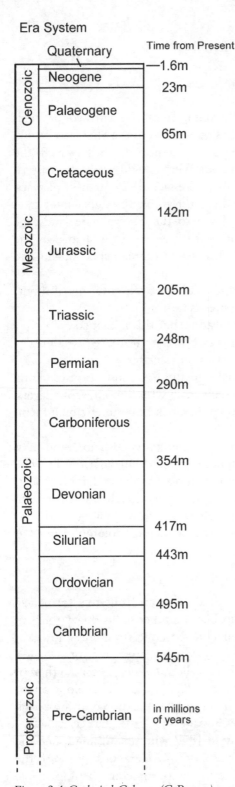

Era System

Quaternary

Time from Present

Era	System	Time from Present
Cenozoic	Neogene	—1.6m
		23m
	Palaeogene	
		65m
Mesozoic	Cretaceous	
		142m
	Jurassic	
		205m
	Triassic	
		248m
Palaeozoic	Permian	
		290m
	Carboniferous	
		354m
	Devonian	
		417m
	Silurian	
		443m
	Ordovician	
		495m
	Cambrian	
		545m
Protero-zoic	Pre-Cambrian	in millions of years

Figure 2.1 Geological Column (C Rayner)

relationship between the formations but showed that the Sheinton Shales fauna, nearly all from the Sheinton Brook, was of Tremadoc age (at that time assigned to the Cambrian Period).

Detailed work by Stubblefield and Bulman (1927) confirmed Calloway's results and refined his correlations. They extended the faunal lists and established zones based on particular fossil assemblages. More detail of this can be seen in the section on Sheinton Brook. However, it should be emphasized here that during the deposition of the fine muds that eventually became the Sheinton Shales, our parish, which of course did not then exist, would probably have been located at latitude 60-65 degrees south on the northern edge of the vast continent of Gondwanaland. The well-preserved trilobite fauna suggest quiet, well-oxygenated, fairly shallow seas.

Sheinton Brook

The brook starts its life as Hughley Brook, just west of Church Preen, then becomes Harley and eventually Sheinton Brook as it enters the respective parishes. It meanders backwards and forwards across a variety of rock types, mainly flowing through the Lower Silurian succession, typical of Sheinton Parish.

Within the parish, it is the section through the Sheinton Shales that is of national importance, colour photo 2.3, (centre section).

Why is this? It has the best exposures of the upper division of the Sheinton Shales and is the original source of the rich fauna of the Conophrys (formerly Shumardia) salopensis zone and of the microfossil flora used by Rasul in 1979 to define part of his acritarch zonation (figure 2.2).

Figure 2.2 Map to show zones in the Sheinton Shales, especially Conophrys pusilla zone (after C J Stubblefield & O M B Bulman, 1927)

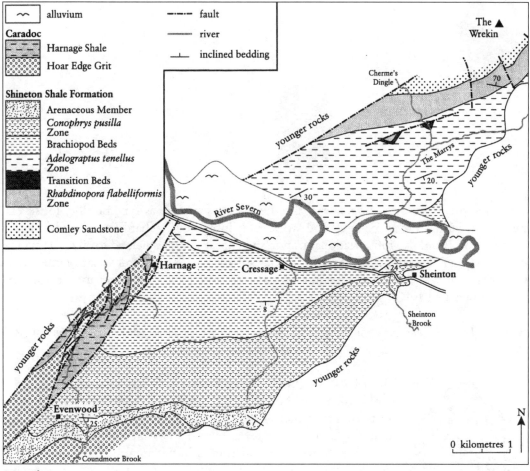

Map of zones

Both of these provide a standard for correlating Upper Tremadoc strata internationally. It is not, therefore, surprising that the site was designated as a Site of Special Scientific Interest.

There is another reason for its importance.

Trilobites moulted annually (like snakes) until they were fully grown and so it was possible for a single individual to be fossilized several times at different stages of maturity. Along Sheinton Brook moulted exoskeletons, recognizable by the absence of eyes which were not shed, have been found in a state of good preservation displaying excellent detail. The most important discoveries were the complete suite of growth stages of Conophrys salopensis, which Stubblefield described in 1926 and from which he drew important general conclusions about growth in trilobites (figure 2.3).

Asaphellus homfrayi
True size 6cm

Conophrys pusilla
True size 5mm

The good preservation of the material and the site's designation as Type Locality for several species has led to further research and work on trilobites by Richard Fortey and others. So Sheinton Brook is of international importance because it has yielded fossil fauna typical of the Upper Tremadoc Series, now re-classified as Lower Ordovician rather than Cambrian, for which it is still a prime reference section. Hence its designation as an SSSI and an important RIGS site.

Figure 2.4 Dimorphoconus granulatus: reconstruction of supposed living appearance (after S K Donovan & C R C Paul)

You've heard of the Loch Ness Monster! What about the Sheinton armoured worm? In the Sedgwick Museum in Cambridge is the prize collection of specimens from the Sheinton Shales. C R C Paul, when examining some of these, discovered an extra, unknown one, a mere 10mm x 8mm of 65 spines. Its affinities are uncertain but this tiny fossil seems closest to a group of armoured worms, formerly classified as Machaeridia, and has been given the name Dimorphoconus granulatus. It is the world's only known specimen. **It Came From Sheinton Brook!**

The Silurian in Sheinton

There is a 55 million year gap between the deposition of the Sheinton Shales and the Kenley Grit. In Sheinton parish most of the Ordovician rocks are missing, having never been laid down there. So at the beginning of the Silurian Period we would have been part of a land mass lying east of the Central Wales Basin of marine sedimentation, still about 25 degrees south of the Equator. The early Silurian is known as the Llandovery epoch and was a time of encroaching seas. By mid-Llandovery times the sea had transgressed eastward and the coarse sediments of the Kenley Grit were deposited unconformably on the Sheinton

Shales (figure 2.1). It has a maximum thickness of 65m. Today the Kenley Grit appears as a yellow-brown coarse sandstone or grit with conglomeratic horizons containing rounded pebbles derived mainly from the Uriconian Volcanics of Pre-Cambrian age, colour photo 2.4, (centre section).

The only fossils recorded are poorly preserved Lingula erumena – a brachiopod. This suggests a shallow marine environment of deposition typical of a shoreline, perhaps even a lagoonal one, often associated with restricted fossil communities. In Sheinton and villages nearby, especially in Kenley itself, this rock can be seen as a distinctive, attractive building stone.

The Kenley Grit is succeeded by finer sediments of the Pentamerus Beds and Hughley Shales. Although the Pentamerus formation often consists of sandy shales and blue mudstones, there are bands of a very distinctive shelly limestone, packed with the brachiopod fossil, Pentamerus oblongus (figure 2.5).

Figure 2.5 Pentamerus oblongus, Llandovery Series – true size 3.5cms (after British Palaeozoic Fossils, as above)

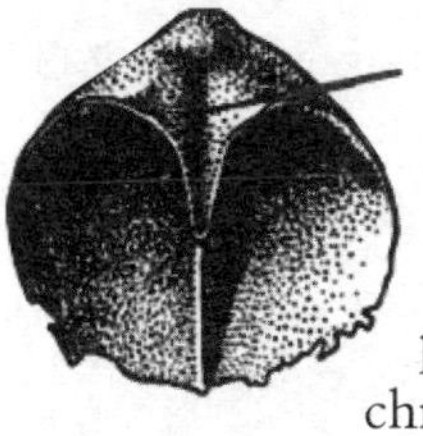

Spondylium

The brachiopod is so-called because a central plate, the spondylium, divides the shell into 5 chambers. When the organism becomes fossilized, the spondylium produces an arrow-shaped appearance. The arrow shape was commonly used in the past as an identifying symbol on prison uniforms and government supplies so Victorian geologists christened the Pentamerus beds, *Government Rock*. The maximum thickness of these beds is 150m.

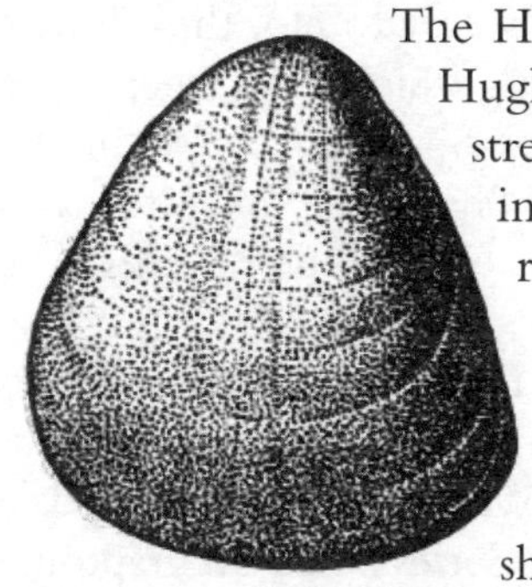

The Hughley Shales (max. 175m.) have their Type Section along the Hughley stretch of the brook, near the village of that name where a stream bank has SSSI status, having been recognized as being of international importance and the standard stratigraphical reference site. In Sheinton parish, however, these rocks outcrop across the western part of Buildwas Park but are poorly exposed only in stream sections. They consist of inter-bedded purple mudstones and thin calcareous sandstones with a range of fossils that indicate deposition in the deeper part of a continental shelf. It is thought that the sandy layers resulted from rapid deposition induced by storm surge currents. Palaeontological *depth* indicators - brachiopods and trace fossils - suggest deposition well offshore in deeper but still relatively shallow seas. Fossil assemblages in the Hughley Shales include the brachiopods, Clorinda and Stricklandia, typical of the deeper shelf environment.

In their study of the Llandovery rocks, Ziegler and colleagues recognized 5 distinct fossil communities characterized by brachiopods, which represented a different depth of water. The key brachiopods are shown in figure 2.6.

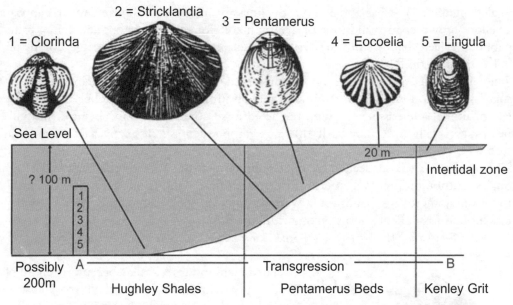

1 = Clorinda
2 = Stricklandia
3 = Pentamerus
4 = Eocoelia
5 = Lingula

Sea Level
20 m
Intertidal zone
? 100 m
1
2
3
4
5
Possibly
200m
A
Transgression
B
Hughley Shales
Pentamerus Beds
Kenley Grit

Following marine transgression from A to B a sequence of rocks at A
will contain the five brachiopod communities indicated

Figure 2.6 Early Silurian, Llandovery epoch. Brachiopod communities, representing increasing depths of water (after Ziegler) in order of water depth.

It is difficult to be sure about absolute depths but it is thought that there is a range of at least 200m. As a result of these observations, it has been relatively easy to plot the advance of the shoreline, in other words, the Llandovery Marine Transgression, as a deeper sea community replaced a shallower one. This can be inferred in Sheinton parish in the progression from Kenley Grit, to Pentamerus Beds, to Hughley Shales. The Sheinton area in late Llandovery-early Wenlock times (figure 2.1) was situated on the outer shelf of the Midland Platform (figure 2.7).

By the time the Wenlock Shale, described thus by the famous Roderick Murchison, was being deposited, the depth of the sea was uniform and the outcrop is therefore continuous from Ironbridge to Ludlow. The formation is thickest under Wenlock Edge in Apedale where Basset et al. in 1975 defined 2 new stages in the Wenlock Series based on graptolite fauna, called the Sheinwoodian and Homerian. They also divided the Wenlock Shale Formation into the Buildwas and Coalbrookdale Formations, the latter including the Farley Member. All this demonstrates how important the Sheinton area has been for establishing global stratigraphical boundaries in the Silurian Period.

At Buildwas the Llandovery-Wenlock boundary occurs in the bed of the Severn with the Buildwas Formation overlying the Hughley Shales. This is somewhat inconvenient for any geologist wishing to study the boundary so the international strato-type for the base of the Wenlock Series is at Leasows on Hughley brook. There is, however, a much poorer exposure of the same boundary actually in our parish in Buildwas Park where, with an eye of faith, it is just possible to distinguish between the purple and grey-green shales.

The Buildwas Beds comprise grey and olive-green soft siltstones and shales, in places

Standard Chronostratigraphy		Graptolite Biozones	Much Wenlock Type Area Lithostratigraphy	Telford District Lithostratigraphy
Stages	Chronozones			
Homerian	Gleedon	? ? ? Monograptus ludensis	Much Wenlock Limestone Formation	Wenlock Limestone
Homerian	Gleedon	Gothograptus nassa	Farley Member	Wenlock Limestone Reef Facies/Benthall Beds
Homerian	Whitwell	Cyrtograptus lundgreni		Tickwood Beds
Sheinwoodian		C. ellesae	Coalbrookdale Formation	Coalbrookdale Beds
Sheinwoodian		C. linnarssoni		
Sheinwoodian		C. rigidus		
Sheinwoodian		Monograptus riccartonensis		
Sheinwoodian		C. murchisoni	Buildwas Formation	Buildwas Beds
Sheinwoodian		C. centrifugus		

Figure 2.7 Classification of Wenlock strata (after Bassett, M, 1989)

containing small shelly fossils. There are also nodular, calcareous layers and thin cream-coloured horizons of bentonite clay. Although this stratum does not at first seem so because the specimens are small, it is very fossiliferous and there is more variety of species than in the underlying rocks. Corals, trilobites, orthocones, graptolites and brachiopods all occur. One of the most notable fossil collections from the river bank at Buildwas is that of George Maw, the 19th century tile manufacturer from Jackfield. He had the Buildwas fossils extracted by the ton (not to be contemplated these days!), then washed, sorted and picked over for fossils by paid workers. This retrieval process yielded countless specimens for study by specialists of the day. *'From one cartload no less than 4300 specimens of Orthis biloba (figure 2.8) were obtained besides a much greater bulk of other brachiopods, amounting together to 10,000*

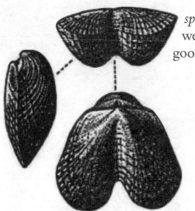

specimens' (Davidson and Maw,1881). Many palaeontologists were subsequently very grateful to Maw for providing such a good collection for their research.

Figure 2.8 Orthis biloba, Wenlock Series. True size 7mm

Through some 3-9 metres above the highest nodular horizon of Buildwas Beds there is a transition into compact olive-grey to dark blue-grey mudstones that lack shelly fragments. These fine-grained, dark limestones comprise the lower Apedale member of the Coalbrookdale Formation, best exposed in the road cutting on the Farley road. However, back in Sheinton parish, there is yet another important geological site, in Whitwell Coppice. Here, the international standard section for the base of the Homerian stage of the Coalbrookdale Formation has been established. It is easily by-passed and in no way spectacular, just a series of small exposures in the banks of a tributary of Sheinton Brook. Yet we have here another SSSI in the parish of Sheinton (figure 2.9).

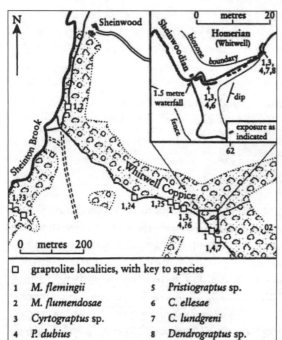

graptolite localities, with key to species

1 *M. flemingii*
2 *M. flumendosae*
3 *Cyrtograptus sp.*
4 *P. dubius*
5 *Pristiograptus sp.*
6 *C. ellesae*
7 *C. lundgreni*
8 *Dendrograptus sp.*

Figure 2.9 Whitwell Coppice, Apedale. Location of the standard section for the base of the Homerian Stage, coincident with the base of the Whitwell Chronozone, together with graptolites recorded from strata above and below this base (after Bassett, 1989a).

The rock types throughout the greater part of the Wenlock succession reflect an uninterrupted continuation across the Welsh Borderland of the Llandoverian marine transgression. Throughout most of the period the area lay well off-shore of the Midland Platform in a low-energy environment. The big change came when a high-energy carbonate sea spread from the east and south-east. This gave rise to a late Homerian shallowing of the sea and the deposition of limestones and the formation of reefs which we associate with Wenlock Edge.

The very eastern boundary of the parish runs along the part of Wenlock Edge below Farley Quarry where the Much Wenlock Limestone is exposed. The capping of the Wenlock Edge escarpment is formed of grey-white limestone (maximum thickness 29m) with shaly partings. Within the limestone are highly fossiliferous Silurian patch reefs, seen as rounded, unstratified masses within the more regularly bedded surrounding rock. These can be seen clearly in the old Farley Quarry and in other quarries along the Edge. The reefs reflect the environmental conditions at this time, which encouraged an abundance and variety of organisms: reef-building corals and stromatoporoids, reef-binding stromatolites, and the crinoids, brachiopods, trilobites and gastropods that lived and fed within the reefs. The sea was clear and warm with plenty of oxygen that sustained a richness of life (figure 2.10) and can be compared to the Caribbean today. Our latitude during the Wenlockian was 15-20 degrees south of the Equator, well within the Tropics.

Figure 2.10 A reconstruction of life in the Silurian Sea (after John Norton, courtesy of the Shropshire County Museum Service)

CONCLUSION

It can be concluded that Sheinton parish and its immediate surroundings has considerable geological interest and importance in its variety of rock types over a small area which reflect the spreading, deepening and then shallowing of the Silurian seas. There are SSSIs and RIGS emphasizing unique exposures of international and national importance. Many of these look insignificant, even boring to the uninitiated, and they are all on private land. It must be stressed that these sites are of the highest geological importance and are very fragile. They must be conserved for future serious research.

GLOSSARY OF GEOLOGICAL TERMS

ACRITARCH . . . . Organic microfossil of uncertain affinity, found in marine sedimentary rocks and having smooth or spiny texture.

BENTONITE . . . . A clay derived from the alteration of glassy, volcanic debris, usually tuff or ash.

CONE-IN-CONE STRUCTURE   Rock structure resembling a series of concentric cones, sometimes mistaken for a fossil. Special pressure conditions seem to be responsible for most, but they are associated with concretions in the Sheinton Shale.

CONCRETION . . . . Large nodule found in shales, limestones and sandstones. It is usually harder than the surrounding rock. May be formed by chemical precipitation on the sea floor or around a central nucleus during diagenesis.

DIAGENESIS . . . . The sum of all changes, physical, biological, and chemical to which a sediment is subjected after deposition.

RIGS . . . . Regionally Important Geological Site.

SPONDYLIUM . . . . A vertical plate, Y-shaped in cross-section, inside the pedicle valve of some brachiopods, to which muscles were attached.

SSSI . . . . Site of Special Scientific Interest.

STAGE . . . . Time unit based on bio-stratigraphic zones considered to approximate to deposits that are equivalent in time.

TILL . . . . Material, usually unstratified, deposited directly by ice sheets. Formerly called Boulder Clay, it contains a wide range of grain sizes from clay to boulders.

TYPE LOCATION . . . . The location in which a strato-type is situated and from which it usually takes its name. It contains the TYPE-SECTION.

TYPE-SECTION . . . . Sequence of strata originally described as constituting a STRATIGRAPHIC UNIT and which serves as a standard of comparison when identifying geographically separated parts of the unit.

STRATIGRAPHIC UNIT . . . . . . A stratum or body of strata recognizable as a unit that may be used for mapping, description, or correlation. It does not constitute a time-rock unit.

STRATO-TYPE . . . . An original or later designated Type representative of a named stratigraphic unit or boundary. It is standard for defining or recognizing a particular unit or boundary.

STRATIGRAPHY . . . . Branch of geology concerned with all the characteristics and attributes of rocks as they exist in strata, and their interpretation in terms of derivation and geological background.

UNCONFORMITY .... A break in the sequence of strata in an area, that represents a period of time during which no sediment was deposited.

ZONE .... Smallest bio-stratigraphic unit based on unique assemblage of fossils and named according to one specific short-lived species. It is the smallest unit on which global correlations can be established.

REFERENCES

Bassett, M, *A Global Standard for the Silurian System,* 1989

Benton, M J, & Gray, D I, *Lower Silurian distal shelf storm-induced turbidites in the Welsh Borders – sediments, tool marks and trace fossils,* 1981

Brenchley, P J, & Pickerill, R K, Animal-sediment relationships in the Ordovician and Silurian of the Welsh Basin, *Proceedings of Geological Association* Vol 104, 1993

British Natural History Museum (Geology), *British Palaeozoic Fossils,* 1975

Cocks, L R M, Woodcock, N, et al, Llandovery Series of the Type area, *Bulletin of British Natural History Museum (Geology)*

Cocks, L R M, & McKerrow, W S, Review of the distribution of the commoner animals in Lower Silurian marine benthic communities, *Palaeontology* Vol 27, pt 4, 1984

Donovan, S K, & Paul, C R C, A new possible armoured worm from the Tremadoc of Sheinton, in Shropshire, *Proc Geol Ass,* Vol 96, 1985

Fortey, R, *Fossils, Key to the past,* 1990

Fortey, R, & Owens, R M, A trilobite fauna from the highest Sheinton Shales in Shropshire & a correlation of the latest Tremadoc, *Geological Magazine,* Vol 128, 1991

Stubblefield, C J, & Bulman, O M R, Shineton Shales of the Wrekin District, *Quarterly Journal of Geological Society,* Vol 83, 1927

Toghill, P, *Geology in Shropshire,* 1990

Ziegler, A M, Silurian marine communities and their environmental significance, *Nature* Vol 207, 1965

Ziegler, A M, Cocks, L R M, and Mc Kerrow, W S, Llandovery transgression of the Welsh Borderland, *Palaeontology,* Vol 11, 1968

3
DIGGING INTO SHEINTON'S PAST

Mike Rayner

As far as is known, no one has previously literally dug for Sheinton's past history. For nearly all the helpers too, it was our first taste of any archaeological work, whether fieldwalking, assisting with (or watching) geophysical surveys, metal-detecting, digging or sifting for artefacts. A wide range of people turned up on various, usually cold and wintry days, from infants to the elderly, and all made useful contributions, including some archaeology students from Belvidere School in Shrewsbury. We were guided by professionals, primarily Hugh Hannaford of the Shropshire Archaeology Service, his assistant Tony Hanna, and the County Finds Officer, Peter Reavill.

The following abbreviated account is drawn almost entirely from Hugh Hannaford's report commissioned by the Sheinton Heritage Group.

Archaeological and historical Background

The Severn valley and its terraces were probably major migration routes for herds of big game during the Mesolithic (Middle Stone Age), c10000-c4500BC, and hunter-gatherers would have followed them. But although Sheinton sits firmly on these routes, no stone tools of that period have yet been discovered here. The first farmers – from the Neolithic – have left some stone tools and flint-making waste in Shropshire, in particular a flint axe at Sheinton Hall Farm. From the succeeding Bronze Age Sheinton has produced a fragment of mid-late copper alloy axe and a bronze chisel. But despite the existence of several ring-ditches in neighbouring Cressage, an indication of the presence of a Bronze Age community in the immediate area, Sheinton has revealed no similar evidence of burial sites.

The earliest known prehistoric site in the parish lies partly beneath the old Severn Valley Railway line on the edge of a river terrace near Sheinton Hall Farm. It is a crop-mark enclosure measuring about 85m x 70m and prior to excavation (see below) was thought to represent a farmstead or small village dating from somewhere between the late Bronze Age and the early medieval period. There are numerous such sites in Shropshire and along the Welsh Borders. The Roman town of Viroconium (Wroxeter) points to a strong Roman presence in the area, manifested in many ways including roads, camps and forts like that by the ford at Cressage, and villas like that at Yarchester, just below Wenlock Edge. No Roman site has yet been identified at Sheinton, however, though numerous Roman items including coins, brooches and lamps have been found, especially in the Sheinton Hall Farm area.

The many later sites of archaeological interest include the church and former rectory on a distinctive promontory – a possible motte-and-bailey location – and a late-medieval/early modern farmstead beside the brook at Sheinton bridge.

Two digs in 2005

The quality and the sheer quantity of significant archaeological finds in the parish prior to the establishment of the Sheinton Group were among the reasons for the Heritage Project's approval for Lottery funding. Helped by support from Hugh Hannaford and Peter Reavill, the group was granted substantial financial backing for archaeological investigation including geophysical surveying and professional overseeing of excavation work. It was decided to carry out preliminary evaluation of three fields to the north of Sheinton Hall Farm, towards the River Severn. Two sites were then chosen for excavation: the crop mark enclosure bisected by the Severn Valley Railway and the top of the field immediately below the church and former Rectory.

Crop mark enclosure
Systematic field walking under Hugh Hannaford's direction produced some Romano-British pottery though with only a slight concentration to indicate likely settlement or other features in the crop mark area. A geophysical survey, however, found a strong magnetic anomaly probably caused by the fill of a ditch on the site of the crop mark. This finding confirmed our inclination to cut a trench across the ditch (A on figure 3.1).

Figure 3.1 Sheinton Heritage Group's archaeological study area 2004-5. Excavation trenches at sites A & B (redrawn by Trevor G Hill from H Hannaford, Sheinton Archaeology Report, 2005 and the geophysical survey)

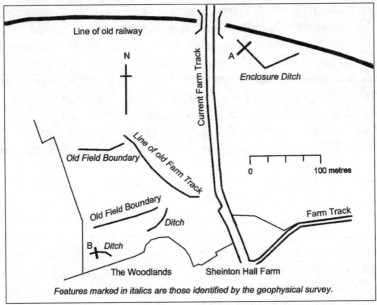

In February 2005, a group of volunteer diggers from the Heritage Group began a five-day dig under the kindly supervision of Hugh Hannaford and Tony Hanna, colour photo 3.1, (centre section).

A trench was cut across the line of the crop mark to reveal a v-shaped ditch 3.5m wide and 1.5m deep (2.0m deep from present ground level) and filled with a series of sandy and sand-silt deposits with varying amounts of gravel, all indicating a gradual silting up. No re-cutting of the ditch was evident and no finds were recovered from the lower fills of the ditch. However, the remains of a Severn Valley Ware vessel embedded in yellowish clay (possibly decayed organic waste, perhaps cess pit deposits) were found higher up in the fill.

The upper fill held a few small sherds of Romano-British pottery including sherds of white-coated pottery of possibly 1st century date. The ditch fills were sealed by a field layer containing more Roman pottery and four prehistoric worked flint flakes.

The size of the enclosure when compared with other excavated examples in the region suggests a later Iron Age rather than Romano-British date, the only Romano-British finds being from the 1st–2nd centuries.

This trial excavation leaves unanswered questions: the precise extent of the enclosure north of the railway line; and the possibility that some deeper-cut internal occupational or other features might survive in the relatively good ground conditions in the enclosure within the crop mark area.

Below church and rectory

Both geophysical surveys and metal detecting were carried out in the field below the church and former rectory. Peter Reavill (the Portable Antiquities Officer for Herefordshire and Shropshire) supervised the metal detector sweep in December 2004 and Hugh Hannaford plotted the many finds. Most interesting were the twenty musket balls and one pistol ball concentrated immediately below a break in the slope of a promontory; much larger numbers had previously been collected from the field, suggesting a possible target butts site dating from any time between the Civil War and the Napoleonic Wars. A single, probably halfpenny, 1790 trade token was turned up, issued by John Wilkinson, the Broseley Ironmaster at a time of a temporary national copper coinage shortage; many companies produced such tokens which between 1787 and 1797 were used much more widely than in the company's shop alone, colour photos 3.5 and 3.6 (centre section), show some of the finds made in the years prior to the work of the Sheinton Heritage Group.

The geophysical survey, colour photo 3.2, (centre section) revealed features including ploughed down remains of two field boundaries and a recently filled hollow way. One other feature with the appearance of a wide ditch might have been of prehistoric origin so it was decided to cut a trial trench, colour photo 3.3, (centre section).

The Group dug the trench in May 2005 but disappointingly no trace emerged of any feature resembling the geophysical anomaly (B on figure 3.1). Nevertheless, an irregular-shaped pit in the trench produced a few large sherds of a jar in very hard-fired Roman pottery with an orange fabric. A further piece of this pottery was found 0.5m away on the surface of the subsoil, this time with three conjoined fragments of Black-Burnished Ware, colour photo 3.4, (centre section).

Archaeology 2006

Following the work in 2005 it is planned to carry out further archaeological exploration on sites already examined. There is potential within the parish for more such work on even more promising sites.

REFERENCE

Hannaford, H R, *Archaeological Investigations at Sheinton, Shropshire 2004-5* (Shropshire County Council Archaeology Service Report Number 241), 2005

4
MEDIEVAL SHEINTON

Trevor G Hill

The Domesday landscape

In the aftermath of the Battle of Hastings the troops of Duke William marched across Saxon England and in areas like Cheshire and parts of north Shropshire left a trail of devastation behind them. In 1085, within nineteen years of the initial invasion, the king sent commissioners all over England to assess his newly acquired kingdom. As a result two surveys were conducted. One reported on the land held by the great lords; the other dealt with each township or estate contained within the local hundred courts. By 1086 a group of monks, probably from Durham, had written up this amazing survey that covers much of England and which we call the Domesday Book. It contains the earliest written record of the settlement called Sheinton and although it was designed as a document for tax assessment, and one should approach its cryptic comments with caution, from it we can discover something about the state of this manor at the time of the Norman Conquest.[1] The Domesday Book records how prior to the Norman Conquest the area which became the manor of Sheinton had been held as three estates by Saxons called Azor, Algar and Saewulf who were described as 'free men'. We can only speculate how these three estates fitted into the landscape but as Figure 4.1 shows it is possible that this area later became the manor of Sheinton, including an estate called Shinewood and another known as West Coppice which at a later date became part of the manor of Buildwas (figure 4.1).

Figure 4.1 The probable Saxon landscape around Sheinton (Trevor G Hill)

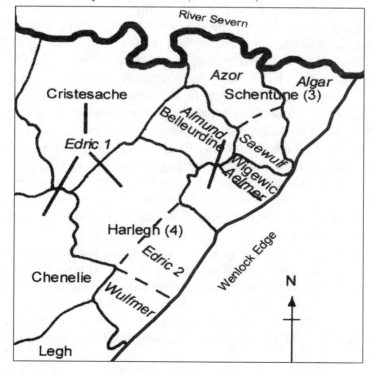

By 1086 the manor of Sheinton was held by Helgot, so he can be regarded as the first Lord of the Manor. He held his land under Ralph de Mortimer who in turn was a sub-lord under Earl Roger or Roger de Montgomery as he is better known. From this time Sheinton continued as one manor with a freehold estate within it known as Shinewood. As Shinewood may have been one of the Saxon estates it appears to have continued free from manorial control. The fact that Domesday records a *francig* - a Frenchman or freeman - suggests that he may have been the holder of the Shinewood estate.

The Domesday book does not record all the land within a manor, for example it does not mention commons, pasture or meadow land but as these were essential ingredients for a farming community it is conceivable that they already existed in the manor. As an assessment for tax purposes more valuable assets such as the arable land and woodland were listed and the extent of land in Sheinton was recorded as two hides. The manor in 1086 included the demesne farm that was occupied by the local lord and which had sufficient arable land for one and a half plough teams. The records also show that on the demesne farm there were two *servi*: men who were bound to their lord and unfree . There were also nine *bordarii* having two ploughs with one additional plough possible. The bordars too were unfree tenants of the lord who would have had a small amount of land which they cultivated for themselves but they also had to give service to their lord. They had two plough-teams (each consisting of eight oxen) so they were involved in arable farming and the further additional plough-team suggests that there was potential for more land to be taken into production. Sadly the cryptic records of Domesday cannot be safely converted into acres but clearly arable land was extensive.

The Domesday Book also records a watermill valued at 10s per annum which would have been located on the Sheinton Brook. Whether this was located at Shinewood or on the Brook Farm site which later became a 17th century iron forge is not known. The record shows that there was sufficient woodland to keep a hundred pigs and there was and still is an area of woodland to the south-east of the parish.

The adjacent manor of Belswardine was also held by Helgot and within the Condover Hundred he also held Harley and Preen together with seventeen other manors in Shropshire. By comparison to Sheinton the Belswardine manor was small, with only half a plough in lordship and another half a plough held by 2 *bordarii*. Apparently it had potential land for 2 ploughs. Its land for tax purposes was only half a hide.

The record shows that under the Saxon King Edward the Confessor Sheinton had been valued at 17s per annum but by 1086 this had been increased to 20s per annum indicating that it had not been ravaged by the Norman troops. Its rise in value suggests that the Norman overlords not only saw room to expand the arable production but that some improvements had already been achieved. Belswardine manor, however, formerly valued at 10s, had fallen to 4s by 1086.

An analysis of the Domesday entries for the surrounding parishes makes it possible to put the manor of Sheinton into a wider picture (figure 4.2). This shows it was located on the eastern boundary of an extensive area of arable land along the Severn Valley. It was in the arable area that extensive open-field husbandry developed, some of which may have already existed from the 10th century. To the east and south on the ridges of Wenlock Edge, Kenley, and the valley of Apedale there was woodland that probably linked to that in Sheinton.

Figure 4.2 The probable landscape around Sheinton at the time of the Domesday Book 1086 (Trevor G Hill)

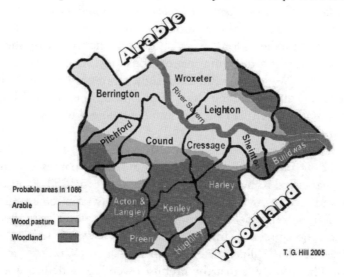

The Manor in the Middle Ages

As the Revd Eyton in his book the *Antiquities of Shropshire* indicates, the ownership of Sheinton Manor matches closely the early history of the manor of Burwarton situated eight miles south of Bridgnorth and located on the eastern edge of Brown Clee Hill.[ii] It too had been held by the Saxon Azor, and after the Conquest Helgot held the manor under Ralph de Mortimer as tenant-in-chief. Subsequently both manors passed into the control of the de Girros family although in Sheinton they did not take up the position of lord of the manor as they did in Burwarton. The Sheinton manor was held by sub-lords who took the name 'de Sheinton'. The earliest appears to have been Hugh de Sheinton who is named as a witness to a charter for Posenhall dated 1150. Throughout the Middle Ages the manor of Sheinton was held by individuals that bore the name of Hugh de Sheinton and it was probably one of their descendants who by the early fifteenth century had taken the surname Harnage.[iii]

Eyton records how the manor of Belswardine followed a slightly different path, falling first under the control of the de Girros family and then under the Lords of Castle Holgate which in the 13th century was held by the Knights Templar, when the tenant of Belswardine was Roger Welcume.[iv] Following Roger Wecume the manor passed down to William de Belswardine, then to William de Baschurch; by 1227 Robert de Clifton and by 1292 to John de Le. Other sub-tenant names are listed in a fine of Robert Burnell dated 18th November 1272: William le Fraunceys and Richard de Clyfton.[v]

At some period in the Middle Ages a carucate of land (about 120 acres) in Sheinton was held by the Abbot of Buildwas and four acres were held by the Prior of Wenlock.[vi] It is probable that the manor/parish boundary was altered later and that these were assarts from the woodland area of the area known as West Coppice.[vii] Today one field located on the parish boundary between Sheinton and Buildwas is still called 'Monks Ridding', a field-name that indicates that the land had been cleared of trees.[viii]

Sheinton and Belswardine were located in Shirlett Forest which was bordered to the west by the Long Forest. In 1235 the surveyors of the Shropshire forests record that *'the boscs of Belleswurthin and Sheinton to be well kept as regarded oak-trees and underwood'*.[ix] In 1260 Hugh de Sheinton was recorded as one of the verderers who attended a Great Forest Inquest. It seems probable that the medieval lords were resident in the manor of Sheinton as there is evidence of the existence of a decaying manor house in the 17th century. In 1318 King Edward II, at his court at Windsor, granted the right of 'free warren' to Hugh de Sheinton and his heirs forever on their demesne lands in Sheinton. This allowed Hugh the right to hunt game on his estate which had previously been subject to Forest Law under which only the king held such a right.[x]

The proof of the existence of sub-tenants or other occupiers of land within the Sheinton manor is limited and we only get occasional glimpses of their names. We know of an Adam de Sheinton who was called to be a juror at a local inquest in 1253. Peter de Sheinton was a juror in 1256 and Adam de la Haye of Shinewood was amerced 12d for vert. This probably refers to a fine in the local court for taking more wood from the lord's land than was allowed by common practice. In 1299 another fine was levied in the manor-court following a dispute between William de Sheinton and his son Walter regarding a house and land in the manor. The result was that the premises were conceded to William for life at a nominal rent of one rose per annum.

A number of 'feet of fines' were listed in the editorial notes of an unpublished Victoria County History that also give some names of Sheinton inhabitants.[xi] In 1294 an Adam de Sheinton was recorded. In 1303 the lands of Adam and Bernard de Sheinton were forfeited to the crown for a year and a day as punishment for some misdemeanour. In 1305 their names again appear when they were outlawed for a felony, the nature of which was not stated, but as the crown was involved and the area was under Forest Law it is probable that this was an offence of taking the king's game, although Eyton considered that the area had been disafforested by 1300. In 1368 two further 'feet of fines' indicate some ownership or interest in land within the manor by Adam Fitz Thomas de Botiler (knight) and Richard Steward de Kymburleye and Hawisia his wife. Richard held one third of the manor and the advowson of the church (the right to appoint the parish priest).

A boundary dispute arose in Belswardine in 1256 when Richard son of Robert de Clyfton took Richard of Harley to the assizes for trespass. He claimed that Richard had entered the wood of Belswardine, beaten his men and carried off timber. Richard de Harley denied the case arguing that in fact the wood belonged to him. As a result the county sheriff ordered that the boundaries between the two manors should be surveyed and four knights were given the task.

In 1290 a form of taxation known as 'The Lay Subsidy' was introduced which resulted in a list of names being drawn up of those liable to pay tax. This tax was also known as the *'tenths and fifteenths'* because it taxed property owners on the basis of one tenth of the value of property held in a town and one fifteenth for property in rural areas. Sadly although the taxation continued after 1334, no later personal names were recorded.[xii] Table 1 shows that in 1327 the Lay Subsidy Roll for Sheinton contained six entries.[xiii]

Table 4.1 **The Lay Subsidy for Sheinton 1327**

Tax Payer's Name	s	d
Hugh de Sheinton	3	0
Petronilla de Sheinton	1	6
William o' Watier	1	0
John o' Constantine		8
Richard le Freeman	1	0
John de la Bolde	1	1

This indicates that by far the richest landowner in Sheinton was Hugh de Sheinton the Lord of the Manor. The author suggests that Richard the Freeman was probably the resident of the separate estate of Shinewood. Further it would appear that Petronilla was the wife, or widow of William de Rugge who now held the house and property of Adam de Sheinton mentioned above.

The Lay Subsidy for Belswardine for 1327 shows four taxpayers: John de Longgeley (paying 9d); Thomas de Wyke (6d); Hugh Hendemo (9d) and Hugh le Stonehewer (6d).

In 1411 another Feet of Fines mentions William Banastre and his wife Margaret who held one third of the manor of Sheinton and the advowson of the church. It is possible that it was he who gave his name to Bannister's Coppice. This wood featured in the Wars of the Roses at the time when the Duke of Buckingham went into Wales to raise an army to fight against Richard III. The rebellion was put down by the king and in 1483 the Duke of Buckingham was betrayed by his steward Bannister and subsequently taken to Shrewsbury where he was beheaded without trial. Various claims have been made in other Shropshire parishes for the place where the duke was captured but it may well have been in Bannister's Coppice.[xiv]

By the 15th century other documents give indications of Sheinton residents, for example in 1448 Hugh the younger son of William Sprott of Cressage deceased was granted land in Cressage and Sheinton and in 1479 appears to have sold the land in Sheinton to William Littleton.[xv]

By the Middle Ages roads had begun to develop in the area. In 1102, following the revolt of the baron Robert of Belleme, King Henry I amassed troops at Wenlock en route for Shrewsbury. When the troops began to cross Wenlock Edge they were ambushed and retreated. As a result they felled many trees on a section of Wenlock Edge to build a new road. The author believes that the route where the troops were ambushed was Blakeway Hollow, the old way to Harley through a very wooded area.[xvi] As the road over Wenlock Edge to Sheinton is fairly clear of trees it is conceivable that this was the new route created by King Henry. Another road through Sheinton was developed to provide a link from Buildwas Abbey to its grange farm at Harnage in the parish of Cound. These two roads came together in the village and then jointly headed for Cressage (figure 4.3). The land for Harnage grange was gifted to the monks of Buildwas Abbey in 1232.

Figure 4.3 The Manor and Parish of Sheinton in the Middle Ages (Trevor G Hill)

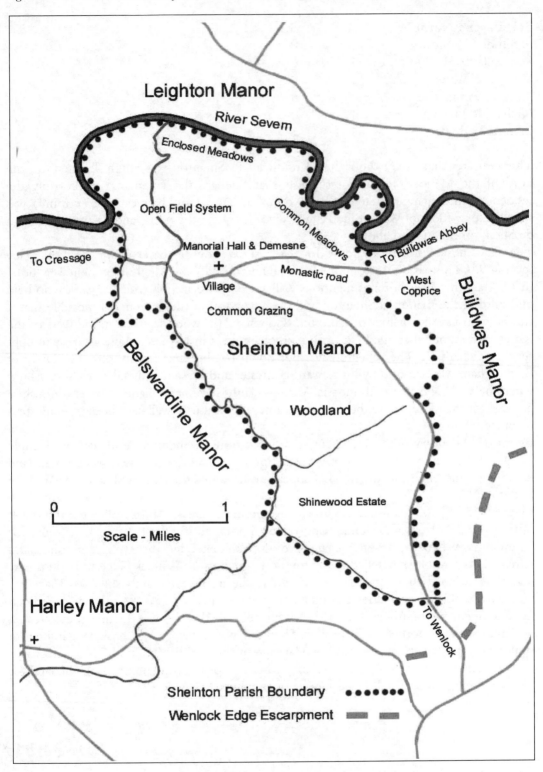

The Parish Church in the Middle Ages

The earliest record of a priest holding the living of Sheinton church was in 1200 when Henry a clerk of Sheinton was recorded as owing six shillings and eight pence for a pourpresture. This was a fine for either erecting a house on any part of the King's demesne, a highway, a common area, or else for the unlawful appropriation of anything that ought to have been available for the benefit of all in the manor. We do not know the details but it is probable that this was for the erection of a house on the common land of Sheinton. As will be shown later the parsonage was located on the north-west edge of the Sheinton Common. In 1272 the Assize Roll makes mention of a parson of Sheinton, named Roger, who also held land in Cressage, but Sheinton was not included in another document that can give us details of the development of a parish church - the Taxation of Pope Nicholas of 1291.

It is believed that the earliest fabric of the present church dates from the 14th century and we find references to the church and its incumbents from this time.[xvii] In 1301 John de Sheinton was presented to the living when still a youth. However, in view of his tender age the bishop sent him to school and for a time the archdeacon was given custody of the church and its future incumbent. In 1303, on the presentation of Hugh de Sheinton, young John was instituted to the living as a sub-deacon and appears to have held it until his death in 1335. His successor Thomas de Withiford was admitted to the incumbency by Hugh de Sheinton and by December 1336 he was recorded under the title of rector. He was, however, granted a four-year licence of non-residence to be a student and he eventually died in 1345. In spite of this evidence Sheinton was not apparently assessed as a separate parish in the ecclesiastical taxation of 1344, known as the Ninth, unless it was the place listed as Shevyn which was assessed for thirteen shillings and fourpence. Eyton continues his list of incumbents by showing that Thomas appears to have been followed by Reginald, son of Walter le Scryveyn of Shrewsbury. Reginald resigned the living in 1349 and was followed by William de Grafton as a chaplain, suggesting that he did not have the full rights of a rector. William de Grafton was admitted at the presentation of John, Lord of Sheinton and rector of Edgmond which suggests that the continuous run of the name of Hugh as the lord may have been broken.

The next rector, John Judas, who died in 1373 was succeeded in December of that year by William Hines. It appears that by this time the advowson, that is the patronage and right to present men to become the parish incumbent, was divided. The patrons were listed as Edward Burnell, Richard de Harnage, Richard de Moreton and Richard de Berwick. William Hines was succeeded by Sir William Hunt who died in 1401 and in April of that year Sir John Wyle was appointed by the patrons who were now Hugh Harnage, Roger Patrick, Thomas de Lee, William de Lee, John de Eynton, Sir William Nicholls (chaplain) and William Boterell. In 1408 and 1410 deeds show that William Wyke, who was gifted land in Eton Constantine, was the parson of Sheinton.[xviii] A list of incumbents in Sheinton Church includes the following priests who served the parish until the dissolution of the monasteries in 1536-40 under Henry VIII (table 4.2).

Table 4.2 **Clergy serving Sheinton Church in the Middle Ages**

Name of Priest	Dates	Name of Priest	Dates
Sir William London	1420	Sir William Upton	c 1500
Sir Thomas Berwych	c1430–45	Sir Hugh Heylyn	1512–13
Thomas Langham	c 1445	Mr John Kyffen	1513–17
Thomas Kent	c 1460	Sir William Diason	1517–18
Sir Thomas Clerk	c 1468	Sir John Smytheman	1518–49

From a board listing clergy provided by a Mr J G Shenton

REFERENCES

[i] The details about Sheinton and the surrounding area are based upon Thorn, F & C (eds) *Domesday Book No 25 - Shropshire*, Phillimore, Chichester,1986. For Sheinton entry 4,11,1, p256d and for Belswardine entry 4,21,9, p258c.

[ii] Eyton, R W, *Antiquities of Shropshire*, Vol 6, John Russell Smith, London, 1858, p215. This volume is used frequently throughout this chapter. Under the feudal system all land was held under the king by tenants-in-chief and then by a series of under-tenants. Eyton explains this for Sheinton as follows: de Sheinton held the manor of de Girros; de Girros of the Lords of Holdgate; the Lords of Holdgate of Mortimer of Wigmore; and Mortimer of Wigmore of the King.

[iii] Documents which refer to the name Hugh de Sheinton used by Eyton in his *Antiquities* and some discovered since are as follows: The Pipe Roll of 1197; Assize of 1221; the Feodary (Feudal allegiance) of 1240; the Placita (court of justice) in 1243 which also records Rose as the wife of Hugh; as a juror in several inquisitions in the years 1247, 1249 and 1253; the *Rotuli Hundred* (Hundred Roll) of 1255; the Assize of 1256 which also lists William as a son of Hugh; the Forest Inquest of 1260; the perambulation of Pulverbatch in 1283; the Feodary of 1284; Chancery Inquisitions of 1294, 1303 & 1305; a Feodary of 1305; Feet of Fines of 1300 & 1306 in the latter Isabel is named as the wife of Hugh; the *Nomina Villarum* (a tax return listing the number of lords to a vill or township) of 1316; the Shropshire Charter Roll of 1318; the Lay Subsidy of 1327 and a document of Edward III dated 1335. By 1350 the name Hugh appears to have been succeeded by a John de Sheinton but in 1423 there was a Hugh Harnage de Sheinton.

[iv] Castle Holdgate became the caput of Helgot's successors and then passed in turn to the Maudut family, the Knights Templar and the Burnells of Acton Burnell.

[v] It is unclear from the list how the tenancies passed from one to another. Walter de Conde (Cound) by a charter known as a quit-claim passed the tenancy to William le Fraunceys tenant, a messuage and bovate in Bedelswurth (Belswardine). William le Fraunceys of Badeleswurthym gave a moity of one and a half virgates to Robert Burnell. Walter de Conde by quit-claim to Richard de Clifton tenant half a virgate in Bedelwurth.

[vi] Recorded by Eyton as from the *Rotuli Hundred* II, 62 (1255). A caracute was a unit of taxation in the north and equivalent to a hide in the south of England. It was probably about 120 acres, M. Bailey, *The English Manor,* Manchester Univ Press, 2002, p242.

[vii] An assart was woodland which had been cleared for cultivation. M Bailey, *The English Manor,* Manchester Univ Press, 2002, p241.

[viii] Foxall, H D G, *Shropshire Field-names*, Shropshire Archaeological Society, 1980, p29.

ix   The term *boscs* is Latin for woods. See Eyton. The boundary between the Shirlett Forest and Long Forest runs through this area with Wenlock, Sheinton and Belswardine being in the former and Cressage, Harley, Hughley, and Kenley in the latter.

x   Shropshire Charter Roll 1317-18.

xi   'Feet of fines' are a third part of a deed originally drawn up on parchment and divided into three sections. This part was retained among the crown court records (now held in the National Archives at Kew). The author is obliged to David Cox and George Baugh, former editors of the Victoria County History, for access to the files they had assembled in preparation for a future volume. But in 2002 funding was withdrawn; no new editions of the VCH are likely to be published. The VCH editors have therefore supported the writing of a Sheinton history.

xii   Stephens, W B, *Sources for English Local History*, Manchester Univ Press, 1973, pp26-27.

xiii   Fletcher, W G D, *The Shropshire Lay Subsidy Roll of I Edward III, 1327*, Woodall, Minshull, Thomas & Co, Oswestry, reprinted from Transactions of the Shropshire Archaeological Society 1907, pp31-2.

xiv   Mate, C H, *Shropshire - Historical – Descriptive*, Mate's County Series, London, 1906, p208.

xv   Raby Castle records - Lord Barnard Box 4 bundle 9/25 & 9/35 listed by editors of the VCH.

xvi   Earlier writers such as Mumford have assumed that the road was via Harley. Mumford, W F, *Wenlock in the Middle Ages,* Private, 1977, p110.

xvii   Department of Environment List of Buildings, 5/112.

xviii   Shropshire Archives, Shrewsbury Borough Deeds 6000/2852 & 3055, Vol 2.

5
THE DEVELOPMENT OF FARMING

Trevor G Hill

From earliest times agriculture has been the predominant economic activity in Sheinton. In recent years landscape historians and archaeologists have suggested that in many places traces of fields dating back to the Bronze-age can be discovered as underlying patterns of later field-systems. Although some Bronze-age artefacts have been discovered in Sheinton it is not possible to suggest any such pattern exists, although the excavation of a boundary ditch by Sheinton Heritage Group in 2005 suggests that between the village and the river there was the site of an Iron-age farmstead. From the Roman pottery discovered in this excavation and from fieldwalking it appears that this site continued to be occupied during the Roman period.

Whether this pre-historic farm continued is a matter of speculation but it seems highly likely that its field-shapes are reflected in the furlong layout of the Open-field system which probably evolved in the late Saxon period.[1] A geophysical survey across a crop-mark also showed quite clearly the plough-lines of the open-field system. However, the angle of this crop-mark and another reported by the farmer appear to be reflections of an earlier field system. Figure 5.1 shows what might have been the layout of the Iron-age farmstead that was still operating in the Romano-British period.

Figure 5.1 The probable area of Sheinton's Romano-British Farmstead (Trevor G Hill)

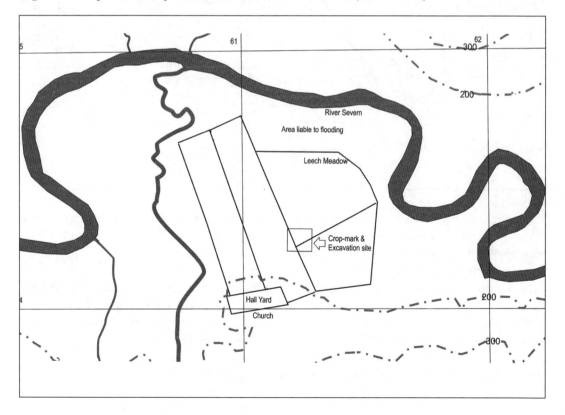

The Open-field system

What is certain is that the farmers of Sheinton practised the Midland Open-field System of agriculture which was probably developed in the 10th century. Under this system of farming three arable fields were cultivated in rotation, two under crops and one allowed to remain fallow each year (figure 5.2).

Figure 5.2 The layout of the Medieval Open-field system in Sheinton (copied, courtesy of the Hon H F C Vane, by Trevor G Hill from an original 1747 map held at Shropshire Archives (6802)

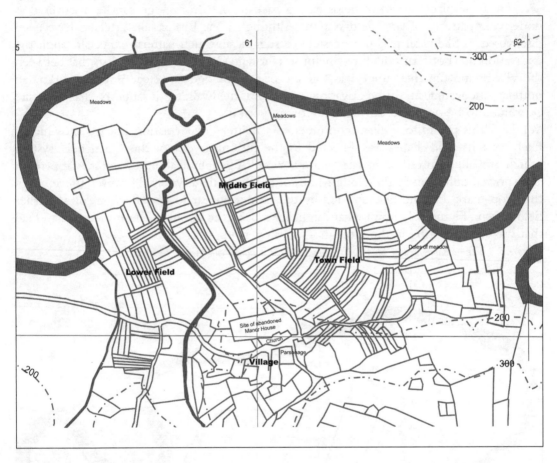

Each of these arable fields was divided into sections known as *furlongs*, which were then divided into strips called *selions*. Both the *selions* and similar *doles* of meadowland, which were alongside the river, were shared out among the lord's tenants.[ii] Under the Open-field System the arable fields were unfenced, but as cattle or sheep were grazed upon the fallow field the control of the movement of the animals was paramount. The task of collecting stray animals lay with the *pinder*, a person appointed each year by the manorial court who would take them to an enclosure called a pound. Sometimes the *pinder* would have an assistant to keep watch over the animals, a lad such as Little Boy Blue

Little Boy Blue come blow up your horn,
The sheep are in the meadow, the cows in the corn.[iii]

The probable layout of the manor of Sheinton during the Middle Ages also included an area of land held by the Lord of the Manor, his demesne farm; the land held by the parson, his Glebe; enclosed fields held by the lord's tenants; and an area of common grazing and woodland, all of which was controlled by the Lord of the Manor colour photo 5.1, (centre section).

At his manor-court it would have been agreed when the lord's tenants and cottagers had the freedom to graze cattle or sheep on the common land and to browse in the woodland. Wood was an important asset in a medieval manor; the timber, that is wood obtained by felling fully-grown trees, was held by the lord himself. The tenants were allowed to gather fallen branches for fuel and, with permission of the court, to obtain wood for buildings, fencing and tools. The probable regime of woodland management in Sheinton was 'Coppicing with Standards'. Under this system timber trees (usually oak) were left to mature while the underwood, such as hazel and beech, was coppiced. Depending upon the end product the coppice was cut to the ground every five to thirty years and the stools allowed to grow a number of new shoots.[iv] This provided a renewable source of wood especially for making charcoal. The name Bannister's Coppice probably indicates that the system was being used for this purpose. In 1235 it was recorded that the oak trees and underwood were well looked after and that in 1256 Adam de la Haye of Shinewood was brought before the court for failing to keep the manorial rules.[v]

Some of the original woodland was cleared to create pasture fields, for a record of 1595 states that in 1511 the Abbot of Buildwas held fields in Sheinton parish namely 'Leech Meadow', 'Hill Ridding' and 'Monks Ridding'. The field-name *ridding* indicates that removing trees had created these fields, and by 1595 they were in the hands of Richard Harnage the Lord of the Manor.[vi] By 1601 these fields and some woodland appear to be have been transferred to Andrew Newport of the Inner Temple and were held subsequently by members of the Newport family.[vii]

In Sheinton the agricultural regime of arable open-fields, meadowland, enclosed fields for pasture, and woodland was followed throughout the Middle Ages and continued into the modern period.

The 1747 Survey of the land in Sheinton held by John Newport Esq

Paul Stamper has stated that by 1750, although much common-land still existed, most of Shropshire's open-fields had disappeared. This was not the case in Sheinton as is revealed by a survey of 1747 and the enclosure papers of 1813.[viii] The details that can be extracted from the 1747 survey show that the farmers of Sheinton appeared to be following the traditional three-field system.

Under a three-field system it can be assumed that the land was primarily under arable cultivation, that two fields each year were used for arable crops with selions, evenly distributed among the lord's tenants and one field laid fallow as Figure 5.2 suggests but by 1747 this appears not to be the case. Figure 5.3 shows that some of the tenants' strips had been amalgamated and some landowners and the church held larger areas of land in the open-fields. Further, Table 5.1 indicates that by 1747 the tenants' land in the open-fields was unevenly shared with the largest amount, 22.11 acres (8.9 Ha), held in the open-fields by Martha Hewlett.

Table 5.1 The acreage of tenants' holdings in 1747

Farm Letter	Tenant	EnclosedAcre	Open-field Acres	Total Acres
A	William Evans	3.91	2.48	6.39
B	Thomas Brown	204.39	19.09	223.48
C	George Hewlett	74.77	15.79	90.56
D	William Pritchard	102.96	3.79	106.75
E	Martha Hewlett	95.09	22.11	117.20
F	Samuel Gittens	29.92	7.47	37.39
–	Thomas Lloyd	5.04	2.11	7.15
–	John Hill	0.80	–	0.80
–	Church Land	9.79	8.81	18.60
Total		**526.67**	**81.65**	**608.32**

The table also shows that Thomas Brown, with a total of 223.48 acres (90.24 Ha), was the principal farmer occupying what today is called Sheinton Hall Farm. The second largest farmer was Martha Hewlett at Church Farm with 117.20 acres (47.35 Ha) and the third, William Pritchard whose homestead was at Leech Meadow, between the open-fields and the river. Apart from William Pritchard's farm and the farm at Shinewood all the farmsteads were situated in the village, which was a typical arrangement in a village that for centuries had practised the Midland open-field system.

By 1747 a sign of the breakdown of the traditional system was the mix of husbandry in the open-fields with arable selions interspersed with pasture. This may have been in place for a number of years as other scholars have noted in the East Midlands.[ix]

Enclosure of Open-fields and Common in the 19th century

Between the Manor Survey of 1747 and the Tithe Survey of 1839 four sources give an insight into the changes that took place in Sheinton's agricultural system.

The first source is a deed of 1771; it records the lease of the Shinewood estate, which was farmed by William Adams and Thomas Harriman, to William Corfield of Harley.[x] In 1779 William Corfield's daughter and her husband Thomas Evans inherited the estate and later in 1806 he commissioned a survey of the estate by G. Longmore (figure 5.3).

The second source, the Agricultural Census of 1801 lists the crops that were being grown and indicates the yields being achieved (table 5.2). This report shows that 205 acres (22% of the total acreage of 946 acres (383 Ha) was in use for arable production. There were 134 acres (54 Ha) of woodland and some 607 acres (64%) of land in Sheinton was being used for pasture or meadow, suggesting that at the turn of the century Sheinton's agricultural economy was primarily based upon cattle and sheep.

Figure 5.3 A plan of the Shinewood Estate 1806 (courtesy of Shropshire Archives, QE/1/2/32)

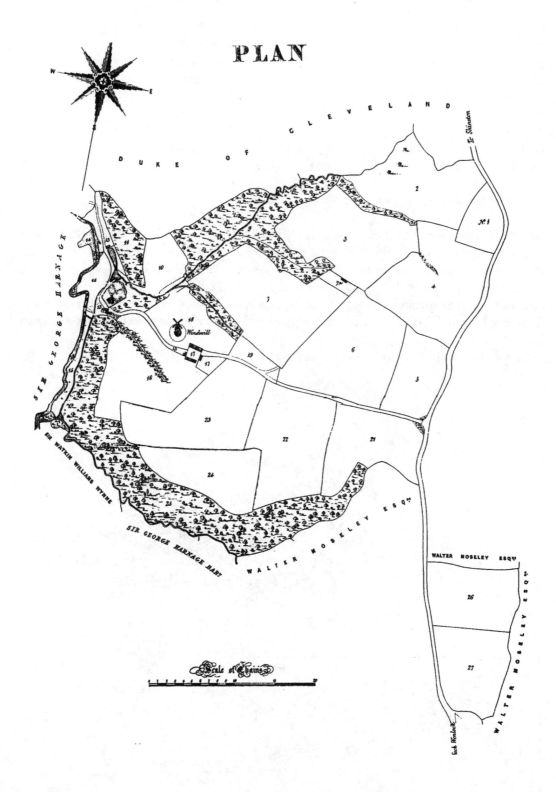

Table 5.2 The Agricultural Census Report of 1801

Crop	Acres	%	Yield per acre
Wheat	85	41	12 bushels
Barley	40	20	16 bushels
Oats	47	23	17 bushels
Potatoes	4	2	
Peas	16	8	13 bushels
Turnips	10	5	
Rye	3	1	17 bushels
Total	**205**	**100**	

Source: The Agricultural Census, PRO HO 67/12, 14 and 21.

The third source is a record of the sale of land by Dr John Littlehales to Walter M Moseley Esq of Buildwas Park in 1806 that included all the Littlehales land in the parish.[xi] The map shows that he held selions in the open-fields; meadow land by the river Severn; enclosed fields, including one behind the church known as Hall Yard; and land on Sheinton Common with its squatter cottages. These selions and common land were still in the hands of Walter Moseley Esq in 1813 when the open-fields and common were enclosed (figure 5.4).

Figure 5.4 Sheinton's Enclosure Map 1813 (courtesy of Shropshire Archives, QE/1/2/32).[xii]

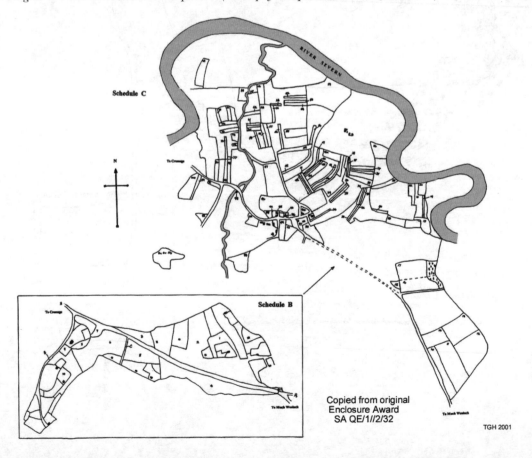

Copied from original
Enclosure Award
SA QE/1//2/32

TGH 2001

The award for Sheinton shows that exchanges took place between the principal landowners, the Earl of Darlington, William Harnage Esq of Belswardine, Walter Moseley Esq of Buildwas Park, and the Rector and Patrons of Sheinton Church.

The Tithe Apportionment of 1839 and Tithe Map of 1841

Since the Middle Ages the land in Sheinton had been subject to an ecclesiastical tax system known as 'The Tithe'. Under this system the church – to support the maintenance of the building, the clergy, and the poor of the parish – collected one tenth of agricultural production.[xiii] However, over the centuries many tithes had been diverted from the local church into the hands of laymen who had been appointed as rectors of a parish church. With the dissolution of the monastic houses the crown not only seized the land but also the tithes that had been granted to the monks by some lay rectors. As a result many parish churches suffered from a lack of tithe income and there was a need to revise the system. Under the Tithe Act of 1836 the collection of the tithe was reorganised as a 'rent charge' based upon the annual price of grain at the London Corn Exchange and the proceeds paid into a central fund for the support of the clergy known as Queen Anne's Bounty.[xiv]

From Sheinton's tithe records of 1839, which also include the Shinewood Estate, it is possible to see how a new layout of land-ownership had developed across the parish. Colour photo 5.2 (centre section) shows how the land had been divided into large coterminous blocks with the Duke of Cleveland holding 617 acres (250 Ha - 65% of the parish). The next largest acreage 192 acres (77.7 Ha) was held by Thomas Evans of Shinewood and 115 acres (46.54 Ha) was held by Walter Moseley Esq. Fourteen acres (5.67 Ha) was still held by the church as glebe and four acres (1.62 Ha), on the boundary of Belswardine, was held by the Harnage family. Apart from land ownership the Tithe records also indicate how the tenants' farms were composed of more or less coterminous fields, colour photo 5.3, (centre section). These records also show how the land was utilised, and as table 5.3 demonstrates the land under arable production had increased from 205 acres (82.96 Ha) in 1801 to 371 acres (149.73 Ha) in 1841, an increase that was at the expense of pasture. This was achieved in part by the improvement of the land by drainage.

Table 5.3 Analysis of Field Types from Tithe records 1841

Field/Area Type	Acres	Hectares	Percentage
Arable	371	150	39%
Pasture	180	73	19%
Meadow	151	61	16%
Woodland	198	80	21%
Waste	13	5	1%
Houses Gardens etc	30	12	3%
Total	**944**	**381**	**99%**

In 1747 the arable land had been mainly confined to the open-field system but by 1839 the tithe records show that arable husbandry had been developed in many fields that were formerly pasture.

Further improvements in the 19th century

Apart from the benefits of enclosure the 19th century also saw other improvements in agriculture such as the rotation of crops, use of lime as a fertiliser and drainage of the heavier land. The latter was an expensive operation which was often undertaken by the landowner. The Victoria County History states that *'by c.1850 it had become the custom either for the landlord to do all the work of draining (except haulage of materials) and charge the tenant 5%, or for the landlord to supply pipes and the tenant to lay them at his own expense under the bailiff's supervision.'* Which of these methods was adopted in Sheinton is not known but we know that as early as 1877 three fields on the south side of the Much Wenlock road (opposite Sheinton Garage) were drained. This drainage scheme was intended to improve the heavy land in this area but according to the present farmers, John and Peter Taylor, the pipes were laid too deep (figure 5.5).

Figure 5.5 The drainage plans of Sheinton Hall Farm (courtesy of John & Peter Taylor).[xv]

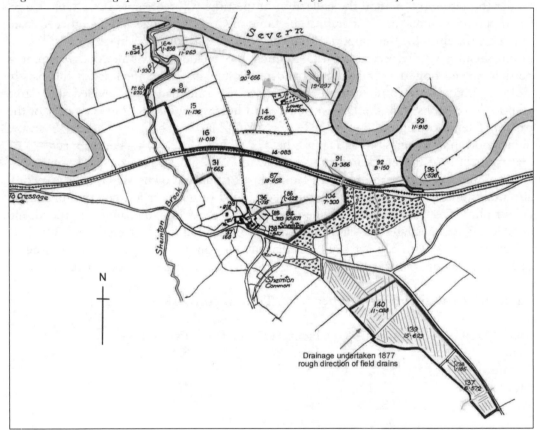

The water from these fields drains into a culvert that passes under the road just west of Sheinton Garage and becomes part of the stream that runs into the River Severn. Figure 5.8 also shows other fields on Sheinton Hall Farm have been drained in subsequent years.

At the beginning of the 21st century farming is still the predominant economic activity in Sheinton. The civil parish, which includes land to the east of the road to Much Wenlock, formerly in the parish of Buildwas, contains four farms, Sheinton Hall Farm, School Farm, Church Farm and Seven Springs Farm which now includes some of the land of the earlier Shinewood Farm.

REFERENCES

[i]   For debate on open-field layout and earlier field systems see Harrison, S, 'Open Fields & Earlier Landscapes', *Landscapes,* Vol 3 No1, Spring 2002; Oosthuizen, S, 'The Roots of the Common Fields', *Landscapes,* Vol 4 No1, Spring 2003; Percival, S D, & Williamson, T, 'Early Fields and Medieval Furlongs', *Landscapes,* Vol 6 No1, Spring 2005: pp47-61 Rippon, S, 'Landscapes in transition: the later Roman and early medieval periods', Hooke D, ed, *Landscape the richest record,* Society of Landscape Studies, Supplementary Series 1, 2000, pp47 - 61.

[ii]   The meadows, mainly on the Severn flood-plain, were subject to periodic flooding.

[iii]   The Opies attribute the rhyme 'Little Boy Blue' to Cardinal Wolsey but more likely it originates in the pinder's control of open-field husbandry. Opie, I & P, eds, *The Oxford Dictionary of Nursery Rhymes,* (Oxford - new edition 1997, p113.)

[iv]   For rods, as used for hurdles or wattle and daub in buildings, 5-9 years growth was sufficient; for charcoal burning up to 20-30 years growth was allowed. Rackham, O, *The History of the Countryside,* 1986, reprinted Phoenix Paperback, 1997, pp87 & 111.

[v]   See chapter 4, Medieval Sheinton. Details of assarting and use of woodland can also be found in Baugh, G C, ed, *Victoria County History – Shropshire,* Vol IV, Oxford 1989, pp41ff, VCH IV is used throughout this chapter.

[vi]   Barnard Estate Catalogue, Vol 1, Deed between 1 Richard Harnage Esq (elder) & Richard Harnage (younger) yeoman & gentleman, both of Sheynton, & 2 William Benyon of Sheynton, yeoman. States: William Walley sometime abbott of Buildwas leased land in 1511 in the lordship of Sheynton to Richard Harnage for 99 years. Calendar of Raby Castle deeds, Box 1 bundle 19, no 40.

[vii]   Barnard Estate Catalogue, Vol 1, Deed between 1 William Benyon of Sheynton, yeoman & 2 Andrew Newport of the Inner Temple, recital of the abbey's lease to Richard Harnage and the assignment of 1595. Calendar of Raby Castle deeds, Box 1 bundle 19, no 41.

[viii]   Stamper, P, *The farmer feeds us all* ,Shropshire Books, 1989, p52.

[ix]   Gray, H L, *English Field Systems,* Cambridge Mass, 1915, p35. Roberts, B K, 'Field systems in the West Midlands', in Baker, A R H, & Butlin, R A, eds, *Studies of Field Systems in the British Isles,* 1977.

[x]   Lease & Release, SA 2089/1/4/25-26. It appears from later sources that by 1779 William Corfield had purchased the Shinewood estate, eg Will of William Corfield SA 2089/1/4/29.

[xi]   Lease & Release, SA 2089/5/2/34-35.

[xii]   Sheinton Land was finally enclosed under the provisions made by The General Enclosure Act 1801, SA QE/1/2/32. Earlier enclosure agreements were made in 1807, SA 2089/6/1/3.

[xiii]   Originally the tithe was collected in kind (eg the tenth sheaf of corn)but over time some land owners agreed to pay in cash per acre. This was known as a modus. In 1752, for example, a Glebe Terrier states that, *'Hugford Hassall of Shinewood paid 5d for a parcel of land called Jack Stocking in lieu of tithe… 1/4d for a tithe of hay in Shinewood Meadow and Walter Acton Moseley paid 12d a year for two pieces of ground in Sheinton'*. Queen Anne's Bounty was set up in 1704 to help with the

maintenance of poor clergy.

xiv   Details of the Tithe Act & the sources it created in: Kain, R J P, & Prince, H C, *Tithe Surveys of England & Wales,* Cambridge, 1985, & Kain, R J P, *Atlas and Index of the tithe files of mid-eighteenth century England and Wales,* Cambridge, 1986.

xv   Thanks to John & Peter Taylor of Sheinton Hall Farm for maps & discussion of drainage systems on their farm.

6
INDUSTRY AND THE RIVER TRADE

Trevor G Hill

Today we think of Sheinton as a small rural parish lying within an agricultural landscape and when we think of industry we tend to look eastwards to Coalbrookdale and the Ironbridge Gorge, sometimes called *The Cradle of the Industrial Revolution*. It is perhaps difficult to realise that in the medieval period the county was covered with small industrial enterprises largely based upon water power.

Mill Sites in Sheinton and the surrounding area

Before the 18th century the power sources available apart from manpower were draught-animals, oxen and horses with pulling strength, wind and water. Whilst draught animals had been used since pre-historic times it was the power of water that was first harnessed by the Greeks as watermills and widely used throughout the Roman Empire, while windmills were introduced into Britain in the late 12th century.[1] At the time of the Domesday Survey (1086) there were ninety-eight mills recorded in Shropshire of which eight were in the area around Sheinton; one each in Sheinton, Buildwas, Leighton, Harley, and two in Berrington and Much Wenlock. Although most watermills were probably built as gristmills to grind corn, once a mill-site had been established it could be used as a power-source for a variety of activities; fulling cloth, making paper, driving hammers in a forge and supplying air for a blast furnace. Along the Sheinton Brook and its tributaries ten mill-sites have been identified (table 6.1).

Table 6.1 Water-powered Sites along the Sheinton Brook

Mill	Parish	Grid-ref	Known Use
Plaish Mill	Cardington	SO 5396	Corn
Holy Mill	Cardington	SO 5595	Corn
Hughley Mill	Hughley	SO 5697	Corn
Kenley Furnace	Kenley	SO 5798	Blast Furnace
Harley Forge	Harley	SJ 5900	Iron Forge
Harley Mill	Harley	SJ 5901	Corn
Wigwig Mill	Wenlock	SJ 6001	Corn
Whitwell Mill	Sheinton	SJ 6201	Corn
Shinewood Mill	Sheinton	SJ 6102	Corn
Sheinton Forge	Sheinton	SJ 6003	Iron Forge

Iron-making in Shropshire

Iron had been produced in Britain since the Iron Age and in some places Roman bloomeries have been identified and excavated.[ii] A medieval bloomery smelted ironstone using charcoal as fuel and produced a lump of iron which after re-heating in a string-furnace could be hammered into wrought-iron. This is called the *'old process'*. The will of

Peter Woodd of Shinewood dated 1567 refers to debts owing to his estate for 'black-stone metal' and 'drosse-metal,' which suggests he may have been operating a bloomery. Gradually water power was harnessed to power the bellows and from the 16th century the blast-furnace was introduced into Britain from continental Europe, the 'new process'. This new technology split the production process into two sites, blast furnaces and forges. The blast furnaces created molten iron which was run into sand moulds and called pig-iron. In the forges the pig-iron was reheated and hammered to create wrought iron. A blast furnace needed four inputs: iron-ore, charcoal for fuel, limestone for a flux that helped remove impurities, and water-power for the blast. The forge needed pig-iron, charcoal for fuel and water power. All these inputs were available in Shropshire. In the 16th and 17th centuries, long before Abraham Darby made Coalbrookdale famous as an iron-making centre, eighteen blast furnaces and twenty-nine forges had been established across Shropshire in the 16th and 17th centuries (figure 6.1). [iii]

Figure 6.1 Ironworks in 16th & 17th century Shropshire (Trevor G Hill, 'The Charcoal-fired Iron Industry in Shropshire from the 16th to the Early 18th centuries', 2003, awaiting publication)

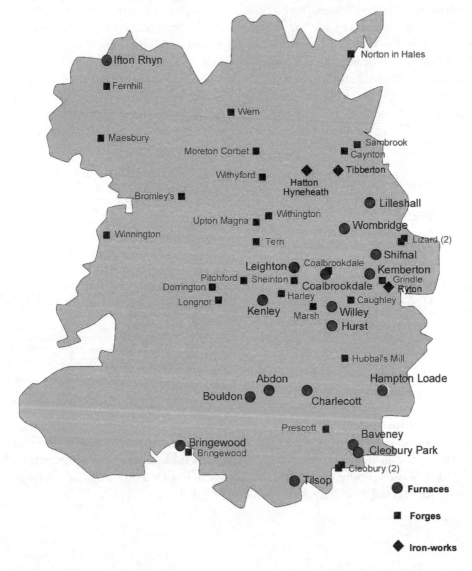

The Sheinton Forge & Leighton Furnace

The two blast furnaces at Willey and Leighton were owned by the Sir Richard Newport (1587-1651) and his son Francis (c1620-1708) together with a partnership of local gentry. One of these partners was William Boycott of Buildwas who was succeeded by his son Francis of Buildwas and Uppington (buried in1696 at Uppington). During the Civil War the partnership supported the Royalist cause by supplying armaments so at the restoration of Charles II the Boycott family was rewarded with the granting of a coat of arms bearing a charge of three grenades. We know that some of these grenades were cast at the Leighton furnace (figure 6.2).

Figure 6.2 (right) The Boycott coat of arms (Trevor G Hill, as for figure 6.1)

The partnership also ran forges at Harley, Sheinton and later at Upton and Longnor. The remains of the blast furnace at Leighton are under the Kynnersley Arms and its car-park.[iv]

Two sets of accounts for Leighton Furnace and Sheinton Forge from the 1680's and 1690's give us an insight into how these linked establishments operated.[v] The furnace drew much of its iron-ore from the Wellington, Dawley Willey and Shirlett areas, and its limestone by packhorse from a quarry near to the Wrekin. An additional supply of iron for smelting called *cinders* was brought up the river, probably from the Forest of Dean. Cinders were the iron-rich residue from bloomeries (the old process). Wood for making charcoal was harvested locally and the charcoal was made very close to the furnace or the forge.[vi] Apart from creating pig-iron the Leighton furnace also made cast pots, small items known as dozenware and forgings such as anvils and hammers.[vii] In 1691 the furnace-man was Francis Edwards and the man making castings was named as John Legus. Some of the pig-iron from this furnace was exported down the river Severn and some was carried across the river to the Sheinton Forge where it was made into bar-iron under the management of Mr Richard Corfield.

The Sheinton Forge accounts show that apart from the pig-iron drawn from the Leighton Furnace it was also buying pig-iron from other suppliers who delivered it to a wharf on the river. In 1692 carriage was paid for ninety-nine tons of pig-iron of which it appears that seventeen tons came from the Willey furnace at £6 -12s - 6d a ton and five tons were *Forest Pigs* at £6 - 10s - 0d. It seems likely that the latter came from the Forest of Dean. We know that there were two forges running jointly at the Sheinton site, a *Finery Forge* that heated the pig-iron and then hammered it into a wrought-iron bloom, and a *Chafery Forge* where the blooms were reheated and hammered into bars. The bars were then exported down the river, some to a warehouse at Bewdley and some to an iron-works situated on the River Stour. The cost of carriage between the river and forge was 6d a ton. In the year 1679-80 the *finer* was paid £52 - 8s - 0d for fining 104 tons 6 cwt and the *hammerman* £40 - 13s - 0d for drawing out 8 tons 6 cwt of bar iron. Various grades of bar-iron were produced by mixing different qualities of pig-iron; those recorded in the accounts were tough bar-iron and mill bar-iron. In 1692 the value of iron sold was £1,187 - 13s - 1d but the profit was only £104 - 7s - 5d. The value of the iron remaining in stock was £1,193 - 8s - 5d but as we do not have the previous year's figures we do not know the value of the opening stock.

Limestone & its transportation from Wenlock Edge

Limestone has been a valuable local asset since medieval times both for spreading on the land to improve its fertility and for making mortar for buildings. As early as 1400 lime was being transported from Wenlock Edge to build Caus Castle and in 1594 sixteen cartloads were delivered to Shrewsbury for building Shrewsbury School.[viii] As has been noted above the introduction of blast-furnace technology in the 16th century increased the demand for this commodity and in 1709 Abraham Darby paid five shillings for six loads of Wenlock limestone for his furnaces at Coalbrookdale. One of the quarries that developed for this trade was on Gleedon Hill, in operation by 1728 although it probably existed much earlier. With the expansion of ironmaking on the East-Shropshire coal-field (the Telford area) during the 18th and early 19th centuries the need for improved transport systems of this vital commodity was paramount. As a result in 1824 William Moseley of Buildwas park assigned *'all those limerocks or quarries of limestone called or known by the name of Glyddon Hill'*. [ix] The deed also allowed the company to build a waggon-way from Gleedon Hill to a wharf situated on the river Severn near to Park Farm (SJ 633042) from where the limestone was conveyed on barges to Coalbrookdale. This waggonway was probably still in use in 1826 when the quarry was sold to the Botfield family but it was certainly superseded when the railway was built from Buildwas Junction to Much Wenlock in 1862 (figure 6.3).

Figure 6.3 The route of the Gleedon Hill waggon-way (Trevor G Hill)

The River Severn and its trade

Although today the river Severn presents a peaceful scene as it meanders through water-meadows along the valley, the accounts mentioned above indicate it was once a major commercial highway. It is conceivable that it was used as a routeway in prehistoric times and it is almost certain that boats would have been used as a means of transport by the Romans. At Wroxeter a riverside site suggests that it was once a quay or a harbour.[x] From the Middle Ages the river was navigable as far as Welshpool although the river traffic between Shrewsbury and Welshpool was sometimes limited by lack of water. Apart from the wharves at Sheinton and Leighton that served the ironworks there were also wharves at Atcham, Cound Lane End, Cressage and Buildwas. Shrewsbury and Bridgnorth were major inland ports where goods from abroad were imported via Bristol and Gloucester and from where the barges and trows carried Shropshire produce to markets down river.

The river vessels were owned by various local watermen such as John Brookes. His barge *The John* operated from Buildwas and it was recorded as taking twenty tons of stone-coal and one ton of iron hammers and anvils to Chepstow in 1697.[xi] It is from the Gloucester Port Books that detailed information can be gleaned. In 1674 the range of goods in addition to iron and coal being transported downstream included cotton and Manchester wares, grain, leather, beeswax, butter, beer, malt, hemp, bark, calfskins and cheese. Upstream went soap, earthenware, French and Spanish wine, brandy and tobacco, lots of it! For example in 1688 'The Charles' of Bridgnorth was carrying 8,400 lbs of tobacco and 'The John' of Shrewsbury carried 16,040 lbs. It seems likely that this was not all sold within Shropshire but was transported by packhorse and waggon to a wider market. In 1758 George Perry, an ironmaster of Lightmoor, recorded that there were 210 owners with 376 vessels working along the river, seven from Welshpool, nineteen from Shrewsbury, and seven from Cound and Buildwas.[xii]

The river through Sheinton was therefore a busy thoroughfare for river traffic. In addition to the wharves there were also fisheries situated along this stretch of the river, five of which are mentioned in the Domesday Book. To catch fish a weir was constructed across the river to a small island called a bylet; between which and the further shore was the *barge gutter* which allowed the barges to pass the weir. Between Atcham and Buildwas there were ten fish-weirs. Before the late eighteenth century the only bridges were at Atcham and Buildwas but the river was crossed by ferries at Wroxeter (the Roman bridge had not survived), Cound-Lane End, and Cressage. A bridge at Atcham had been constructed by the Abbot of Lilleshall to replace the ford and in 1221 a dispute arose about the tolls that were to be charged.[xiii] As a result of a court case it was agreed that the toll for a loaded cart belonging to Shrewsbury would be charged 1d and for all others ½d. The date for the construction of Buildwas bridge is uncertain but it was almost certainly constructed by the monks of Buildwas Abbey for records show that the abbot was granted *pontage*

REFERENCES & NOTES

[i]   The introduction into Shropshire of water-, horse- & wind- mills is found in Baugh, G C, ed, *Victoria County History of Shropshire,* Vol IV, Agriculture, Oxford, 1989, p32.

[ii]   A bloomery was a small hand-powered furnace.

[iii] Hill, T G, 'The Charcoal-fired Iron Industry in Shropshire from the 16th to the early 18th

centuries'. [As yet unpublished paper prepared for the *Revolutionary Players of Industry and Innovation* web-site, 2003. Copies at e g Shropshire Archives, & Birmingham Central Library].

iv   The site featured in a Time Team dig. Some remains can still be seen in the cellar.

v   National Library of Wales, The Leighton accounts - Cilybebyll 2 No 1, 291-2 & 413-5; The Sheinton accounts - Cilybebyll 1293-5, p51.

vi   Although ironstone and limestone could be carried long distances, charcoal could not because the shaking of the panniers on a pack-horse would turn it to dust.

vii   The anvils & hammers were the large ones used in the forges to convert pig-iron to wrought iron bars. The hammers weighed 5 cwt 3 qr each & the anvils 8 cwt.

viii   Hill, T G, Draft article awaiting publication entitled 'Lime Quarries on Gleedon Hill - the waggon-way to Buildwas' (2005). Copy held at Ironbridge Gorge Museum Library.

ix   Shropshire Archives 1681/184/1.

x   White R, & Barker, P, *Wroxeter - Life and Death of a Roman City,* 1998, revised edn, Tempus, 2002, pp99 & 101.

xi   Gloucester Port Book database, reference 1252/17/08/03.

xii   *Gentleman's Magazine,* vol 28, 1758, p277. Quoted by Trinder, B S, in *The Industrial Revolution in Shropshire,* Phillimore, 1981, pp61-62 to which he adds *'and by the early 19th century another writer estimated that the number of boats was double that by Perry'* .

xiii   Harrison, D, *The Bridges of Medieval England,*

COLOUR SECTION

Sheinton Heritage Group – Geology Walk

L–R: Megan Revell, Patrick Kirby, Lyn Pearson, Patrick's friend, Dee Revell, Barbara Thompson, Chris Rayner, Roger Thompson, Brian Pearson, Trevor Hill, Giles Rigby, Brian Revell, Mike Rayner
Photo credit: Brian Revell

1.1 Meanders of River Severn at Leighton. Photo credit: Trevor G Hill

1.2 Buildwas Sands and Gravels. Photo credit: D S Revell

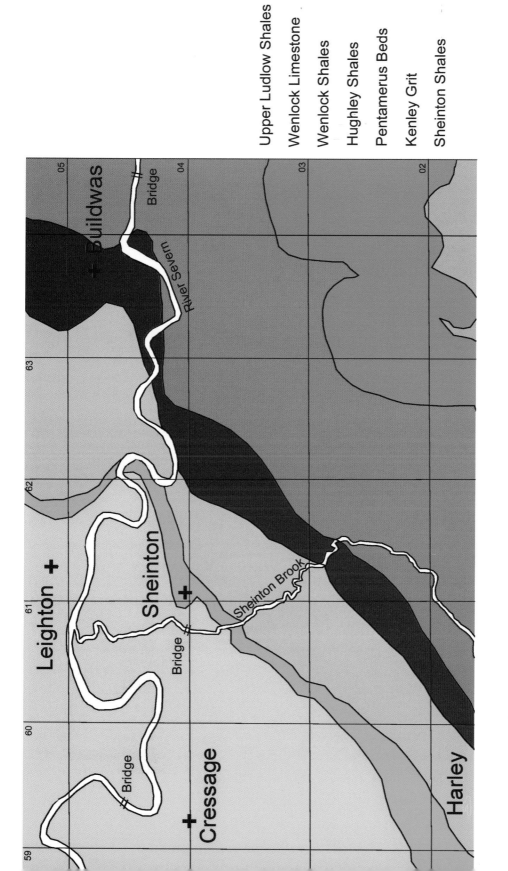

Upper Ludlow Shales

Wenlock Limestone

Wenlock Shales

Hughley Shales

Pentamerus Beds

Kenley Grit

Sheinton Shales

2.1 Geological Map of Sheinton area. Image credit: Trevor G Hill based upon maps of The Geological Survey

2.2 Sheinton Shales with stinkstone concretions. Photo credit: C Rayner

2.3 Sheinton Shales at Plox Brook, Cressage. Photo credit: C Rayner

2.4 Kenley Grit used as a wall stone. Photo credit: C Rayner

3.1 Progress on excavation at site A. Photo credit: Trevor G Hill

3.2 Geophysical survey SHG members try their hand in the area of site B. Photo credit: Trevor G Hill

3.3 The archaeologists discuss the possibility of a ring-ditch at site B. Photo credit: Trevor G Hill

3.4 Roman pottery finds at site B. Photo credit: Trevor G Hill

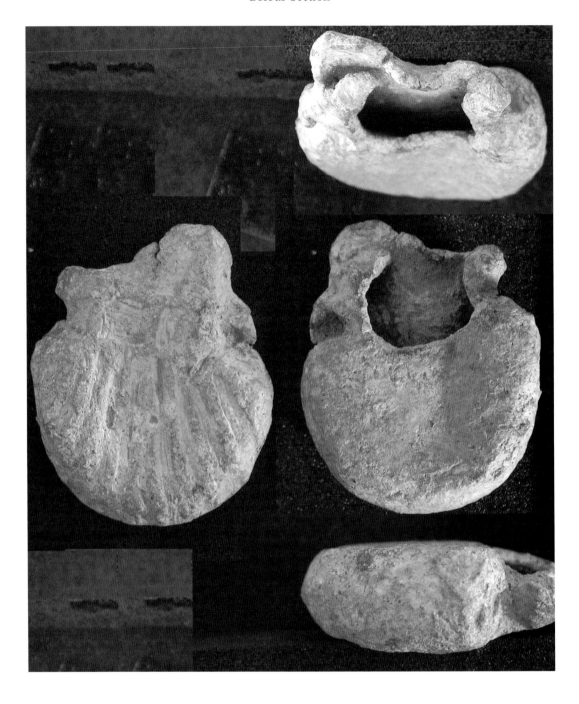

3.6 Lead pilgrim's Ampulla discovered by metal detectorists. Photo credit: P Reavill, Portable Antiquities Scheme

3.5 Bronze-age chisel discovered by Kevin Harvey. Photo credit: P Reavill, Portable Antiquities Scheme

5.1 Sheinton's Open-field tenants in 1747. Photo credit: Trevor G Hill

T.G.Hill 2001

N

Key to Strips

Glebe Land
Thomas Brown
William Evans
Samuel Gittens
George Hulett
Martha Hulett
William Pritchard
Thomas Lloyd

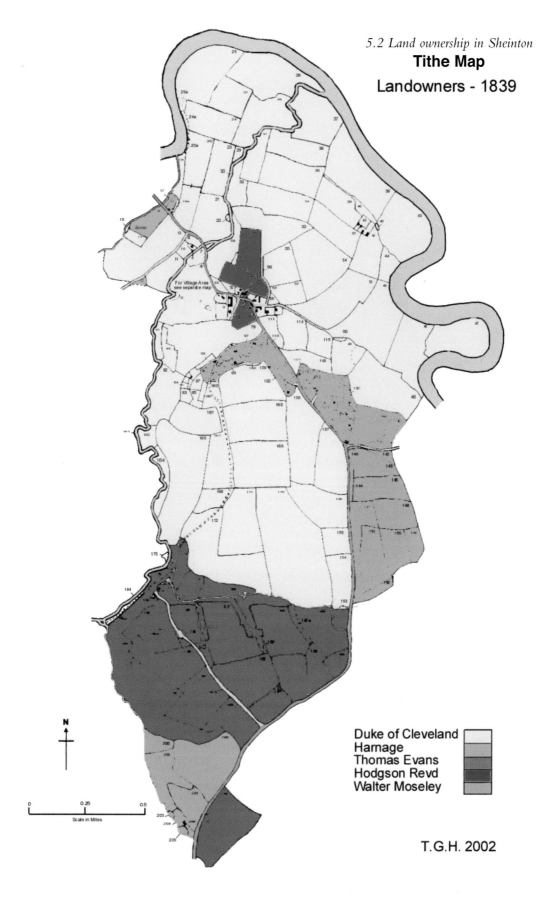

5.2 Land ownership in Sheinton
Tithe Map

Landowners - 1839

Duke of Cleveland	
Harnage	
Thomas Evans	
Hodgson Revd	
Walter Moseley	

N

0   0.25   0.5
Scale in Miles

T.G.H. 2002

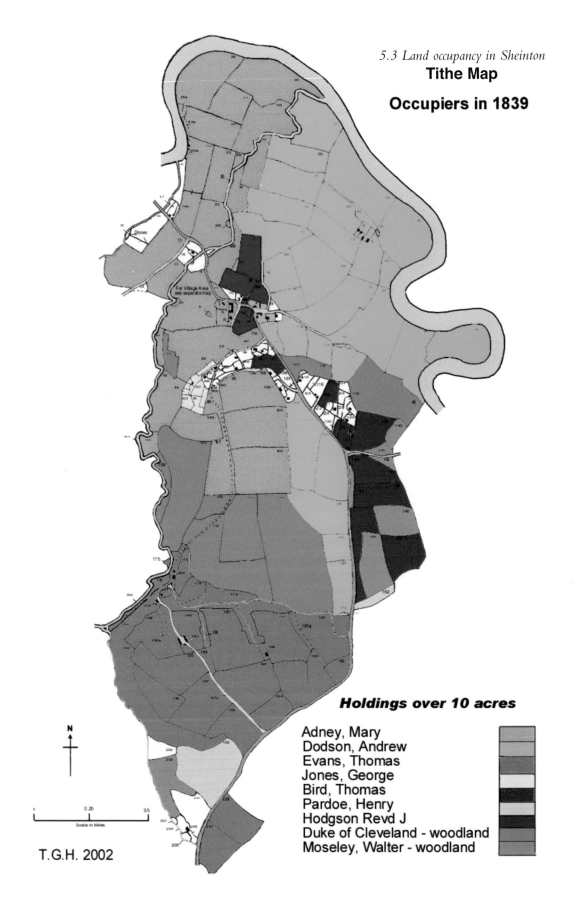

5.3 Land occupancy in Sheinton
Tithe Map

Occupiers in 1839

Holdings over 10 acres

Adney, Mary
Dodson, Andrew
Evans, Thomas
Jones, George
Bird, Thomas
Pardoe, Henry
Hodgson Revd J
Duke of Cleveland - woodland
Moseley, Walter - woodland

N

Scale in Miles
0.25   0.5

T.G.H. 2002

7.1 Sheinton church - Jacobean pulpit. Photo credit: Trevor G Hill

7.2 Sheinton church in 1896, Oil painting by Harriet J Danks

9.1 Sheinton school in 1990. Photo credit: Norman Davies

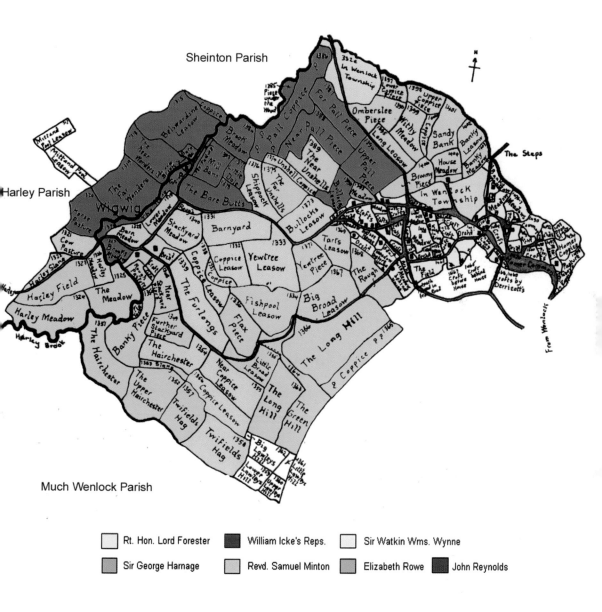

11.1 Land ownership in Homer 1847. Image credit: Trevor G Hill

11.2 Red House farmhouse, detail. Photo credit: D S Revell

11.3 Red House farmhouse bread oven. Photo credit: D S Revell

11.4 Red House Farmhouse. Photo credit: D S Revell

11.5 Homer Farmhouse. Photo credit: D S Revell

11.6 Lawrence's Cottage, Homer. Photo credit: D S Revell

11.7 Homer steps. Photo credit: D S Revell

11.8 Homer steps, detail. Photo credit: D S Revell

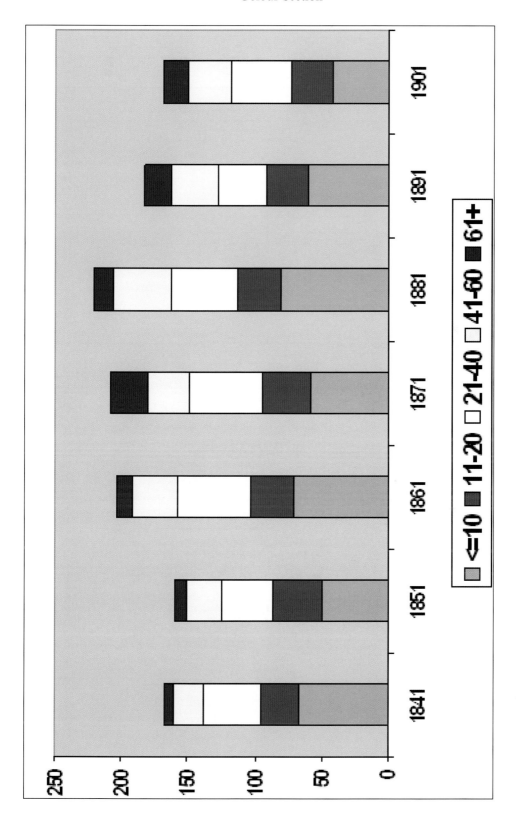

11.9 Homer Population 1841 - 1901 Age structure

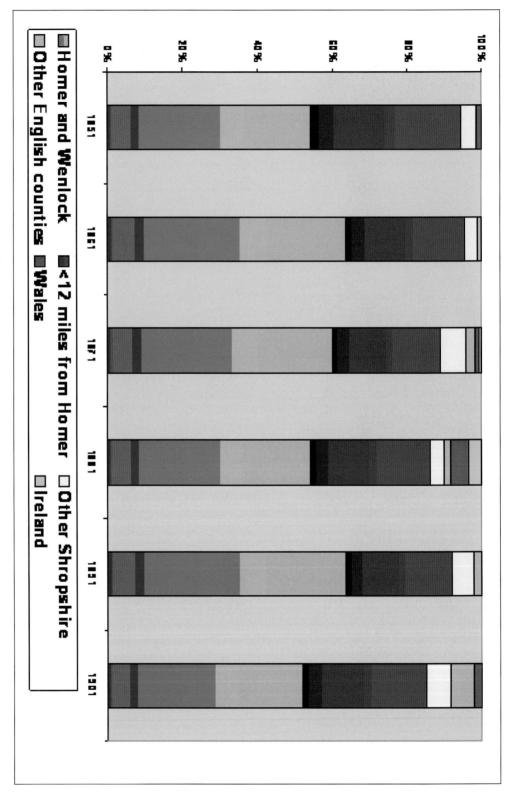

11.10 *Homer population 1841-1901. Place of birth*

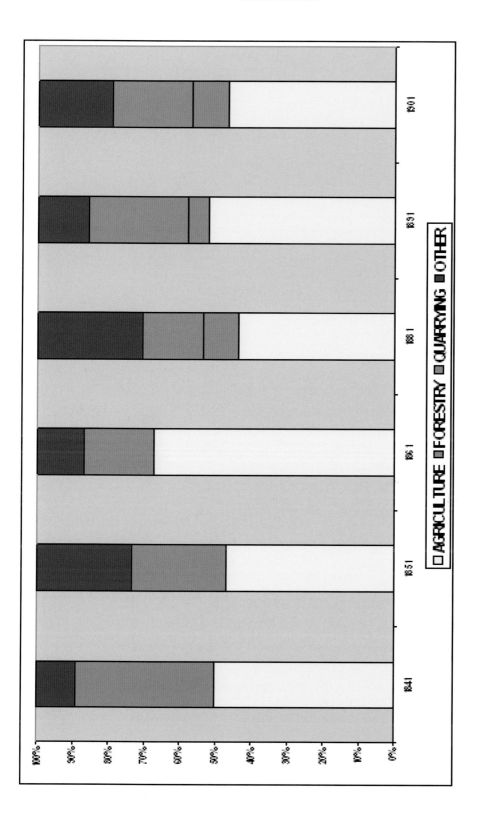

11.11 Homer population 1841 - 1901 Male occupational structure

7
THE CHURCH OF ST PETER & ST PAUL

Trevor and Margaret Hill

Sheinton's most ancient building is its church that stands on a steep knoll dominating the skyline (figure 7.1).

Figure 7.1 Sheinton Church in 1788, watercolour by Revd Williams (courtesy of Shropshire Archives)

From medieval times this small building witnessed the many changes that affected the development of Christianity in England. Throughout the Middle Ages its ministers, rectors, vicars and curates were subject to the control of the Papacy, reciting the liturgy in Latin, and the income of the church was largely supplied by an ecclesiastical tax called the tithe.[1] Also much of the land around Sheinton belonged to three great monastic foundations: Wenlock Abbey to the south, Buildwas Abbey to the east and Shrewsbury Abbey to the north-west, and of these the Abbot of Buildwas had control of some land within the parish of Sheinton. In the mid-16th century all this was to change.

The Reformation

Between 1518 and 1549 the rector of Sheinton was Sir John Smitheman. Whether he lived in the parish is doubtful, he probably merely gathered the value of the great tithe and employed a curate to look after the services in the church. It was during his rectorship that Henry VIII severed the link between Rome and the English church and so The Church of England was born. In 1532 it came under the control of the reforming archbishop Thomas Cranmer and the influence of several continental reformers which ushered in a period of radical change.[ii] However, many of these changes were not felt at local level so adherence to the catholic beliefs and rites continued. Thus in Sheinton when Richard Harnage, Lord of the manor, made his will in 1538, he wrote in true Catholic fashion *'I bequeath my soul unto Almighty God, to our Lord, St Mary and all the holy company of heaven. My body to be buried in the chancel before the image of St Giles of Sheinton.'* This document shows that the chancel still contained an image of a saint though such items would soon be destroyed or painted over as the reformation gathered pace.

Among the changes were the introduction of the English language into services from 1544 and a Prayer Book in English in 1549. This first prayer book was based upon the services that had previously been offered in Latin and accompanied with rituals and traditions such as prayers for the dead and the wearing of priestly vestments. However, by 1552 due to pressure exerted by continental reformers who had settled in England, a revised prayer book was issued.

The introduction of this revised prayer book was overtaken by events. When Queen Mary was on the throne between 1553 and 1558 the church was once again under the control of Rome and the old order restored. How much this affected the church in Sheinton is not known but we need to appreciate that although changes were being made at a higher level for most of the people there was little change, they were still Catholics at heart. From 1549 Sir Edmund Batchelor was the rector and in 1557, after the Marian Persecutions, he was succeeded by Thomas Hardinge.[iii] How long Hardinge continued as rector is uncertain for the earliest Glebe Terrier of 1612 includes the name of William Moryce.[iv] It is probable that if Hardinge was of an extreme Catholic persuasion he was replaced during the early part of Elizabeth's reign when a partially reformed Church of England was restored. However, new continental reforms were spreading in England following the teachings of John Calvin (1509-64) and this was to have a profound effect on the church during the next century.[v]

The Seventeenth Century

When Charles I came to the throne in 1625 the Calvinist influence had grown considerably and there was increasing tension among English Christians. From 1621 William Peake was the rector of Sheinton and he appears to have continued until 1645. It was during his time that a new bell was cast by William Clibury bearing the inscription *'Jesus be our Speede 1623'*. William Peake would have witnessed the appointment of William Laud as archbishop in 1633, the persecution of the Calvinists and a return to more catholic practices. Under Calvinist influence the traditional stone altars had been destroyed and a table placed in the centre aisle of the church around which the people sat for their communion service. Under Archbishop Laud these tables were removed and the altar with altar rails was reintroduced. It was these changes in church practices and the intransigence of Charles I that led to confrontation between the King and Parliament.

The Civil War began in 1642 and three years later Archbishop Laud was beheaded followed by the king's execution in 1649. It is perhaps significant that in Sheinton we find the appointment of George Cudworth in 1645. No doubt he was of a puritanical persuasion, for he remained in post throughout the Commonwealth period and until 1662. He would have been part of radical reforms in the way the Church of England was organised when the hierarchical structure of bishops was replaced along Presbyterian lines with a series of governing courts.[vi] Following the restoration of Charles II in 1660 a compromise was reached for a time between those who espoused Presbyterianism and those who wished to return to the earlier forms of worship. One local minister who became involved with these changes was Richard Baxter whose family home was in Eaton Constantine.[vii] It was at this time that many Puritan clergy resigned or were evicted from their livings and locally this happened in both Cressage and Berrington. Later some of these ministers gathered together dissenting congregations who became known as 'Non-Conformists'.

George Cudworth was followed as rector in 1663 by William Phillips who had been the patron of Sheinton since 1621. After William Phillips came Richard Phillips, gent, in 1686.

Samuel Willis, who in 1666 became vicar of Leighton through the patronage of James Lacon of West Coppice, appears to have also served Sheinton. He was a friend of Richard Baxter and his father, another Samuel Willis, had been a Puritan minister in Birmingham until 1661. Samuel Willis senior spent the rest of his days living with his son in Leighton where he was buried in 1684.[viii] Samuel Willis junior was buried in Sheinton.

It was during these turbulent years that the church in Sheinton was refurbished. This included the construction of box pews, a pulpit with Jacobean carving and the replacing of the church door (figure 7.2).

Figure 7.2 (right) The massive door of Sheinton Church (Trevor G Hill)

This large oak door, which still retains its original strap hinges, probably came from Buildwas Abbey and appears to have been the porter's door. Within it is a small door known as a wicket with a 'peephole' that allowed those within to see those who wished to gain entry. Also a bell was recast by John Martin of Worcester bearing the inscription *'Gloria in Excelsis Deo 1658'*.

The Eighteenth Century

During the eighteenth century the Church of England went through another difficult period that encouraged the rise of non-conformist congregations. Many rectors and vicars were non-resident with some holding many churches and regarding their livings in economic rather than spiritual terms. They tended to appoint curates to look after the needs of a parish and this was certainly the case in Sheinton.[ix] Those listed as rectors and curates in Sheinton are:

Table 7.1 Rectors serving Sheinton Church in the 18th century

Based upon a board erected in Sheinton Church by Mr J G Shenton, the Parish Register, and clergy appointments listed at Lichfield Joint Record Office (B/A/3)

Name of Rector	Years	Other churches & notes
Henry Binnell	1683 –1713	Also vicar of Buildwas & Leighton
William Dicken	1714 –43	Also vicar of Buildwas
George Podmore	1748 –55	
Rowland Chambre	1756	Non-resident
Thomas Lewis	1763 –1771	
Robert Williams	1771 –77	Also vicar of Buildwas
Michael Pye Stephens	1777 – 87	Lived at Barrow
John Holme	1787 – 96	
Townsend Forester	1796 –1803	Non-resident
John Hodgson	1823 – 43	Non-resident

Table 7.2 Curates serving Sheinton Church in the 18th century

Sources as in Table 7.1 above

Name of Curate	Years	Other local churches as curate etc
Samuel Snead	1756	Cound
Stephen Prytherch	1759	Leighton, Much Wenlock
W Williams	1760	
Thomas Greaves	1766	
William Prosser	1766 –1770	Kenley, Cound, Cressage
Richard Dewhurst	1769	
Daniel Hemus	1771	Buildwas, Kenley
William Brownell	1771 –1776	Buildwas
Jonathan Williams	1777	Buildwas

Families who were patrons of the living sometimes appointed their kinsmen to the church as did the Dickin and Stephens families in the 18th century. This did not apparently happen when George Podmore was presented to the living by Elizabeth Dicken on the death of her husband William Dickin.[x]

From Table 7.1 we can see that a number of Sheinton's rectors were responsible for other local churches and some may have held churches in other parts of the country. Table 7.2 shows curates, and vicars of other churches, were also appointed to serve Sheinton. Samuel Snead was appointed as the curate for Rowland Chambre in 1756 and he also served Cound from 1758 to 1766. On the 10th April 1772 the rector Robert Williams sent a report to the bishop stating that he lived in Bridgnorth and employed a curate Daniel Hemus who also served the church in Buildwas and Kenley. Williams allowed him £30 a year for Sheinton.

The report tells us that the living in Sheinton was a poor one and only worth £50 a year, that there were no almshouses, charity school or *'settled donations for the poor'* and that *'the money given at the offering is disposed of to the poorest inhabitants at the discretion of the minister and church wardens'*. Apparently all the twenty-seven families who lived in the parish were members of the Church of England for it was reported that there were no *'Papists or Dissenters'* in the parish. It commented further that as the parish was so small only one public service with a sermon was held each Sunday but additional services were held at the great festivals. When Michael Pye Stephens was appointed by Thomas Stephens of Benthall in 1777 he was non-resident and lived in Barrow, while John Hodgson who was appointed to the living in 1832 also received a certificate of non-residence from the bishop. Clergy who did reside in Sheinton lived in the parsonage house which was situated on the south side of the road opposite Sheinton Hall Farm (the site on which the school was built in 1845). In 1612 the Glebe Terrier described it as *'A house of four bays, with a barn adjoining 4 bays, a small orchard and garden and a little cote or coal house in the inner court or fold.'*[xi] By 1682 the house, which was most likely timber-framed, had been extended to five bays and included a small farm described as *'Barn 4 bays, cart house, stable and tying for cattle 2 bays, little house for swine and poultry in very good repair; orchard newly planted and garden each of about ¹/₂ acre'*. The Glebe Terriers also list the location of arable land in the three open-fields and doles of meadow. In 1698 it is recorded that all tithes were paid in kind except for Leech Meadow which was tithe-free; that Shinewood Farm paid 5d and the mill 2s a year and that John Lacon of West Coppice paid 9d for Foxholes Coppice and 3d for Legg Meadow. As far as a tithe of animals was concerned, in 1698 the rector received one pig, one goose and one lamb out of every seven born; and 1 lb of wool was due, being tithed as lambs. In cash he received ¹/₂d per cow and calf, 1d for every barren cow and 2d for a colt. He also received other cash payments: 2d per communicant at Easter, 1d for every chimney, and 1d for every garden. For services he received 6d for a burial and 4d for registering it, 4d for churching women after childbirth, 6d for registering a baptism, 1s for publishing banns, 1s 6d for a marriage and registering it and 5s for a marriage by licence. For burials in the chancel there was a charge of 6s 8d.

In 1718 the Glebe Terrier states that the rector, William Dicken, was responsible for the repairs of the chancel, the wicket and stile and that the chancel was full of seats.[xii] He himself had a large seat near the north side of the chancel for his wife and family and another for his servants. Because Sheinton was a poor living the rector in 1736 invested £200 in land in Brueton in Audlem Parish to improve Sheinton's income to which a further £200 was added from Queen Anne's Bounty.[xiii]

As well as the seats for the rector and his family in the chancel, the nave was fully pewed and some of those seats were allocated to specific families for a pew rent. In 1700 a question was raised with the oldest inhabitants about certain pews that had belonged to the Harnage family. The enquiry reports:

'Alice Labey saith she doth know ye seats in ye church of Richard Higginson and Thomas Haynes formerly belonging to Francis Harnage and that ye said Francis Harnage had a wife and four daughters, but the said Alice doth remember only ye said Francis Harnage… Edmund Nock saith that he can remember ye said Francis Harnage sitting in the said pew and after his decease Eleanor Harnage, daughter of ye said Francis Harnage did sit in the same pew until the said Eleanor married to Mr Lutwich and then the said Mr Lutwich and the said Eleanor his wife sat in the said pew…'[xiv]

It appears that the Harnage family, then living at Belswardine Hall, attempted to re-establish their right to the pew in 1760 when a letter was written by John Littlehales to W Harnage Esq of Belswardine:

'Wheras a seat in the church of Sheinton (my property) has been occupied by your late family several years (first by permission of my tenant the late Revd Dicken) and no acknowledgement made of me for it, take this opportunity by the hand of Miss Dicken to acquaint you, you are welcome to sit in that seat provided you sign the enclosed memorandum.'

The memorandum was signed by William Harnage on 16th June 1760 acknowledging that the seat was then the property of Lieut.-Colonel Littlehales and that he had granted the Harnages permission to occupy it.[xv]

The Churchwardens' Accounts 1779 – 1809

The Churchwardens' accounts from the late 18th and early 19th centuries give us some useful insights into how the church was financed and what expenditure was incurred. In the pre-Reformation church funds were raised through renting of church land, events such as plays and church ales or the profits of a flock of sheep. From the Tudor Period income was mainly from a church rate based upon the value of property.

Each year the vestry meeting confirmed the appointment of the churchwardens for the following year and set the rate and it is clear that they were well versed in anticipating the next year's expenditure. The rate varied throughout the period from a halfpenny in the pound in 1791 to ten pence halfpenny in 1798, with the average being two pence three farthings in the pound (figure 7.3).

On the 29th May 1778 the churchwarden of Sheinton, Richard Dicken, bought a new book in which to record the Churchwardens' accounts for which he paid two shillings and six pence.[xv] This volume covers the years 1779 to 1809 and during this period the total amount raised from the church rates (called in Shropshire lewns) was £171 – 15s – 2$\frac{1}{2}$d.[xvi] The record shows the names of the ratepayers and how the money was spent. It also shows the debit or credit balances each year that were passed from one churchwarden

Figure 7.3 Graph of income 1779-1809, from Sheinton Churchwardens' Accounts (Trevor G Hill & Margaret A Hill, courtesy of Shropshire Archives, P242/b/2/1/1-2)

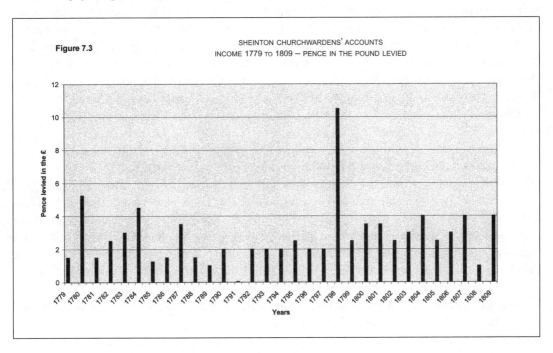

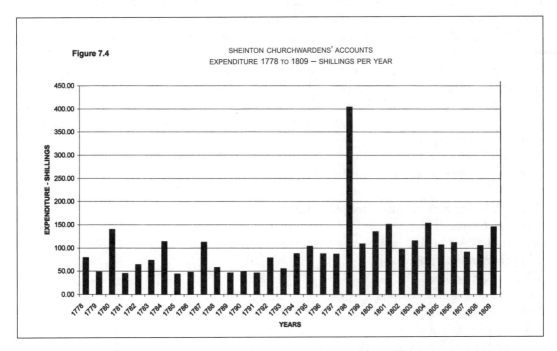

Figure 7.4 Graph of expenditure 1779-1809 from Sheinton Churchwardens' Accounts (Trevor G Hill & Margaret A Hill, as for figure 7.3)

to the next. However, in the years ending 1785, when Richard Beard was warden and 1786, when Richard Dicken was warden, the balances of five and threepence and one and tenpence halfpenny were not carried forward to the next year. One wonders if these two characters pocketed the difference! During this period the total amount paid by Sheinton Hall Farm was £32. The farm was occupied by the Brown family until 1793 and then by Thomas Parry until 1807 when it passed to John Evason. Next in value were Richard Beard's property for which he paid £26 and the occupiers of Shinewood who paid £23. Thomas Cotton occupied Shinewood around 1780 and was subsequently followed by members of the Evans family. Other high ratepayers were the Parton family (£22), John Smithyman of West Coppice (£17) and the Hulett family of Church Farm (£16).[xvii] No documentation has been discovered to allocate a particular farm to the Beard family and it is probable that the Parton family occupied Leach Meadow farm.

As the parish rate was set with the next year's budget in mind, the income in 1798 (figure 7.3) is reflected in high expenditure and figure 7.4 also shows how from 1800 the annual expenditure was higher than it had been prior to 1798. This was due to a growing awareness of the need to improve the church and in particular to look after its fabric. By isolating the figures that relate to repairs to the fabric of the church, the bells and the windows, other years stand out as well as 1798. In 1780 the churchwardens decided to carry out some repairs and whitewash the interior of the church. They spent £3 6s 8d for mending the church and fourteen shillings and sixpence for lime and its cost of transport, no doubt from lime-burners on Wenlock Edge.

In 1784 the high cost was largely the expense for mending the bells with £1 11s 6d paid to Mr Harries and thirteen and eightpence to Wilkinson who no doubt worked under Mr Harries. There was also a payment of two pence for a new tongue for the little bell, six shillings for two new locks and seven and twopence halfpenny for repairing the windows. In 1787 Cliveley was paid fourteen shillings for another cartload of lime and the cost of its transport, and Mr Corbett was paid seven shillings and nine pence for hair which shows that some of the lime was being used for plastering the walls. Other repairs were being undertaken: Cox was paid three shillings for mending the communion rails and Mr Holbrooke £1 17s 6d for his bill, the items not being specified but it has been assumed that this was repair costs.

However, the highest expenditure was incurred in 1798 when some major repairs to the fabric were carried out as shown in Table 7.3.

Table 7.3 Repairs to Sheinton Church in 1798

Item of Expenditure	£	s	d
Mr Tonks as per his bill	13	2	3
100 bricks and carriage		4	0
1 load of lime		12	6
Cost of loading and turnpike charge		13	9
Lime for white-washing		8	0
Mr Cox per his bill		10	1
Thomas Instone for repair of bells		5	2
Total	**15**	**15**	**9**

After all that year's building activity it is interesting to note that the churchwardens paid Elizabeth Hewlett two shillings and sixpence for cleaning the church! The costs for repairs continued in 1799 with Mr Instone receiving another fourteen shillings and a penny and Joseph Cox fourteen shillings and ten pence for repairing the windows. Further work on the bells was undertaken in 1801, and in 1806 they were supplied with new bell ropes that apparently needed replacing again in 1809. Problems with the windows continued in 1802 and 1803, and in 1809 the windows were reglazed at the cost of sixteen shillings. In 1804 Mr Scales submitted his bill of £2 8s 1d for repairing the church and John Instone received another one shilling and eight-pence in 1809, perhaps payment for fitting to the church door a new lock which cost four shillings and sixpence.

Apart from repairs, the regular expenses incurred were for washing and repairing the church linen, bread and wine three times a year for communion services, candles and the costs of the churchwardens at the Visitation of the Archdeacon or Bishop. The ringers were paid two shillings and sixpence for ringing the bells on 5th November each year and in 1783 one guinea was paid for instructing the psalm singers, indicating that music in the form of metrical psalms was part of the worship. In 1790 and 1791 the communion cup was repaired at the cost of a total of one shilling and eight pence and it must have been damaged again as in 1805 they spent a further one shilling and sixpence on its repair. In 1800 R Tart was paid for a new pulpit cloth and in 1803 £1 14s 10d was spent on sacrament linen. At the turn of the nineteenth century this demonstrates that there was already a concern for improvement in both the fabric and the furnishings of Sheinton church.

The Nineteenth Century

The awakening of interest which resulted in the refurbishment of Sheinton Church in the late 18th century was mirrored across many parishes and grew apace in the 19th. Part of the driving force behind this movement was the enthusiasm of John and Charles Wesley and others who saw the need for reform.[xviii] This was of particular importance in areas where the population was rising rapidly. In some there was no provision for worship by the Church of England so this need was filled by energetic non-conformist congregations. This was particularly true in rapidly expanding industrial areas, like the East Shropshire Coalfield, where in the early 19th century many Methodist chapels were built.

As the century progressed the Church of England responded to the needs of the growing population by building totally new churches such as those in Oakengates, Donnington Wood, Ketley, Wrockwardine Wood and Little Dawley or by pulling down and rebuilding existing churches such as Priorslee, Cressage and Harley. Some existing churches were also refurbished or extended of which Sheinton was one. Further, the Church of England became involved in providing schools for the education of the poor.[xix]

The need for a moral framework in this ever-increasing population also taxed the minds of the establishment who feared the possibility of revolution and as the Church of England was part of the establishment it felt that its duty was to respond not just with building but also with a concerted effort to reconnect the church with the people. This revival was twofold: from Cambridge University many priests were fired with evangelical zeal and from Oxford University the Tractarians set in motion a move to revitalise the church by returning to its more Catholic roots. So were born the Low Church and High Church wings of the Church of England. A new emphasis was put on the teaching of the Catechism both in church and in the National Schools where children learned by rote the words *'To order myself lowly and reverently to all my betters… to do my duty in the state of life, unto which it shall please God to call me.'* Words that were re-echoed in a verse of the popular children's hymn, All Things Bright and Beautiful: *'The rich man in his castle the poor man at his gate, God made them high or lowly and ordered their estate.'*

It is against this background that we need to measure the 19th century changes that took place in Sheinton. As we have seen above in the report to the bishop in 1772 there were twenty-seven families in the parish and in 1801 the first census records that in Sheinton there were thirty-four families and a population of 163. In 1841 thirty-six houses were recorded with total population of 154 but in 1851 this had dropped to thirty-one houses and a population of 138. As figure 7.5 shows, apart from 1861 when Sheinton's population increased because the railway was being constructed, it remained fairly stable throughout the 19th century

.

Figure 7.5 Sheinton Population in the 19th century (Trevor G Hill, after population table in Victoria County History, Shropshire Vol II, 1973)

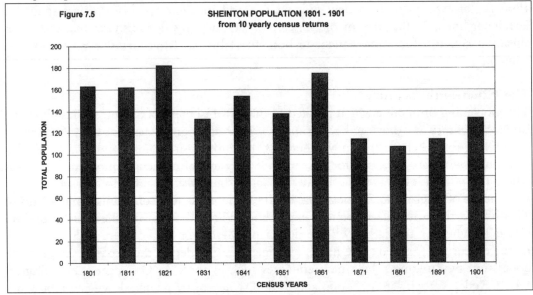

In 1832, during the time of John Hodgson, the parsonage was declared as *'unfit for the residence of a minister'* although it was still shown as a building on the Tithe Map of 1841 and the rector and his family appear to be in residence at the 1841 Census. Apart from the need to refurbish the parsonage, the continuing need for repairs to the church was dramatically realised when in 1836 the whole of the nave roof on the south side slipped off during a service. Thankfully no one was hurt. In 1843 when the Revd Hodgson died he was replaced by Samuel Burrows but only for a year as he also died. But a new enthusiastic rector, Henry Bagnell, arrived on the scene in 1844 and remained in post until 1852. Apart from his activity in the church he was also instrumental in the building of the school that opened in 1847 (see chapter 10). In the Religious Census the Revd Bagnall reported that on 30th March 1851 the church contained eighty rented pews and twenty-two free pews; [xx] fifty-three people attended the morning service and fifty-one in the afternoon, and there was a Sunday school with thirty attending in the morning and twenty-six in the afternoon. Considering that the population in 1851 was 138 the morning congregation represented 38% of the population, and some additional parishioners may have also attended in the afternoon.[xxi]

It was during Bagnall's time that a major rebuilding of Sheinton Church was begun when he launched a fund for its restoration in 1852. Contributions were made by the Duke of Cleveland (£100), Mrs Moseley of Buildwas Park (£60), Sir George Harnage of Belswardine (£20) and other contributions included a grant from the Diocesan Building Society (£40), the Cordon Fund (£40) and the Incorporated Society for Building Churches (£25). The remaining £545 was raised locally through subscription cards and appeals. The restoration was completed under his successor Revd George Burd and a fulsome newspaper report was made about the re-opening of the church in 1854.[xxii] It shows that the total cost of rebuilding the nave, building an additional north aisle, refurbishing the chancel, and alterations to the tower was £830.

The restoration was undertaken by local builders working under the direction of the Shrewsbury architect S Pountney Smith. He reported on the existing building:

'Originally it was a double parallelogram forming a nave and chancel and a bell turret mounted on the west end of the nave. In the 14th century the original chancel appears to have been taken down and rebuilt in a superior manner but of very imperfect materials… Two hundred years later the eastern wall of the chancel and the north and south walls of the nave, together with the roof of the nave were reconstructed in the debased style then prevalent, the original window giving place to the square-headed mullioned form and the roof cut out of the old timbers… Internally the ceiling was "nicely plastered and whitewashed". A few centuries more of neglect consigned the old building to a hopeless mass of dilapidation, and such it was when the late and present rectors commenced their operations.'

As has been noted above the earlier churchwardens' accounts had referred to the purchase of lime for plaster and whitewashing.

On the furnishings of the church the newspaper report says 'The pews having been removed from round the communion table… in the erection of the new pews much care has been taken to retain the old carved oak which was previously part of their construction.' Colour photo 7.1, (centre section) shows the pulpit.

The report continued:

'A neat pulpit and reading desk stand in front of the chancel which is raised some few steps above the nave and it is intended to add an elegant reredos. It is also intended to restore the porch next Spring. Here is a relict of considerable interest to the antiquarian, the south or principal door being the porter's door from the neighbouring ruined abbey of Buildwas.'

The day when the church was reopened was a great event. The report shows that a large procession formed at 11 am led by the Bishop of Lichfield, the Archdeacon and the Reverends Henry Bagnell, George Burd and W S Burd. Listed in the congregation are some forty-six clergy and sixty-five gentry with some accompanied by their family members. Even with the new extension to the nave they must have filled most of the seats in the church and where the local people sat is not recorded; maybe they had to stand outside. Morning Prayer was led by the rector Revd George Burd and was followed by a communion service led by the Bishop. The Bishop also preached a sermon that made reference to the nearby River Severn when he commented that the Gospel was like *'a large river in which there were fords through which a sheep might wade and depths in which the elephant might swim.'* The service was followed by refreshments supplied by the rector for 170 people, served in a tent with the catering undertaken by Mr T Harris confectioner of Shrewsbury. Clearly these refreshments were for the *'better sort of people'*. In addition *'a numerous party of ladies and gentlemen partook of the kind hospitality'* supplied by Mr Andrew Dodson the churchwarden. Again there is no reference to the *'lower orders'* so maybe they had to shift for themselves. The day concluded with another service at 5-30 pm and the total collections for the day amounted to £75 11s 6d which more than covered the outstanding debt of £30 which the Bishop had mentioned in his sermon.

A painting by Harriet J Danks shows the restored church, colour photo 7.2 (centre section) as does an early photograph of the interior (figure 7.6).

Fig 7.6 Sheinton Church interior after its 19th century restoration (from an undated postcard held by M Rayner)

Figure 7.7 (left)
Revd Henry Lee, rector of Sheinton 1878-1907, undated (courtesy of Churchwardens of Sheinton Church)

Figure 7.8 (right)
Revd Henry Lee, his wife & one son standing at Sheinton Rectory Door, undated (courtesy of Churchwardens of Sheinton Church)

The building of the north aisle of the church does not appear to have been justified by any change in Sheinton's population. We can see therefore that its restoration was part of the upsurge of interest in refurbishment led by enthusiastic clergy, for not only was the church restored but a substantial new rectory was built.

At the time of the enclosure of the open-fields and commons various exchanges of land had taken place resulting in the rector receiving a field to the north of the church called Hall Yard in lieu of the strips he had previously held in the open field. This field had in the past been the site of the manor house but had became the rector's glebe land and it was there that the new rectory was built.[xxiii] The census in 1851 shows that it was occupied by Revd Henry Bagnell, and in 1861 by the seventy-year old Revd Benjamin Bailey, his two unmarried daughters, who were born in India, and two servants. Benjamin Bailey became rector on the death of Revd George Burd in 1856 and remained in post until after the census of 1871 and followed by the Revd William Henry Wayne. He was succeeded in 1878 by the Revd Henry Lee who continued as rector of Sheinton until 1907 (figure 7.7). He and his family became closely involved with church life in the area, his sons Henry, John Herbert and Charles also becoming parsons and his daughter, Evelyn, a deaconess who worked among the poor in Notting Hill, London as is recorded in her memorial window.[xxiv]

This chapter has shown that for over three centuries some of the changes that affected the church in England were felt in the small parish of Sheinton. Some clergy had different attitudes to the task of a parish priest and served the parish with varying levels of commitment. The churchwardens' accounts of the late 18th century have indicated how the building had not been properly maintained. It has also demonstrated that a new motivating force was introduced by the 19th century clergy and how this led to the restoration of Sheinton church[xxv].

REFERENCES

i The Tithe was levied in Britain from the 12th century, mainly on agricultural produce: a tenth of the crops grown or animals raised. It maintained the clergy, repaired the church buildings and helped the poor. The rector received the great tithe (arable crops and hay), his assistant – the vicar – the lesser tithe (animals, vegetables, eggs and milk). During the Middle Ages monastic houses and lay lords had gained hold of much of the great tithe. After the Dissolution in 1536, the monastic houses' tithes were transferred to the crown and more then accrued to laymen. As will be seen later another John Smytheman was one of the land occupiers who paid rates (lewns) to the Church Wardens of Sheinton between 1779 and 1809. He was a tenant of the Moseley family and resided at West Coppice (later called Buildwas Park).

ii Including the German exile, Martin Bucer (1491-1551), made Professor of Divinity at Cambridge in 1549.

iii At this time some priests received the title sir but they were not knights of the shire.

iv Watts, S, ed, The Glebe Terriers of Shropshire – Part 2, Shropshire Record Series, Vol 6, Univ of Keele, 2002, pp84-86. Glebe Terriers recorded parish church holdings from 1571.

v The curate at St Mary's, Shrewsbury, was a strict sabbatarian who caused some 'tumultuous behaviour' for several years through his attempts at puritanical cleansing. See Lawson, J, 'John Tomkys & the Catechising of Shrewsbury School, 1580-1640' in Price, D T W, ed, Trans. of the Shropshire Archaeological & Historical Society, Vol LXXVII (2002), pp 85-88.

vi	In 1646 Parliament set up a Presbyterian system of church government. Each congregation was governed by a series of courts which at local level consisted of the minister and elected elders. Coulton, B, 'The fourth Shropshire Presbyterian Classis, 1647-62', in Cromarty, R, ed, Trans of the Shropshire Archaeological & Historical Society, Vol LXXIII, 1998, pp 33-43.
vii	After the Restoration, Richard Baxter was an important mediator between the Presbyterians & those trying to restore the former structure of the Church of England.
viii	By the 17th century the patrons were the Lacon family of West Coppice.
ix	For details of 'non-residence', plurality & the poor state of many parishes in the 18th century see Bettey, J H, Church and Parish – a guide for local historians, Batsford, 1987, pp109-125.
x	From the records of Patrons and Clergy of Sheinton, Lichfield Joint Record Office B/A/3.
xi	Glebe Terriers: surveys of the holdings of a particular church. See Watts, S, ed, The Glebe Terriers of Shropshire – Part 2, Shropshire Record Series, Vol 6, Univ of Keele, 2002, p84.
xii	It will be noted from Figure 7.1 that the chancel was of a better construction than the rest of the church.
xiii	Queen Anne's Bounty: fund set up in 1704 to improve the income of the worst paid livings.
xiv	Shrewsbury Public Library Manuscripts Vol 6, p61.
xv	Shropshire Archives 2089/8/1/1-2.
xvi	No earlier accounts have been found for Sheinton but there are some later volumes.
xvii	A John Smithyman was Sheriff of Shropshire in 1761 and at the time rented West Coppice.
xviii	In Madeley, the Revd John Fletcher, friend of John Wesley, supported reform.
xix	Non-conformist developments in education (by men like Joseph Lancaster with the Lancasterian or British Schools from 1808) caused the C of E to found in 1811 what became known as the National Schools.
xx	The 1851 Religious Census: the government tried to assess the strength of religion in Britain by asking for the number of seats available in every church & chapel, & also the numbers of people who attended church on Census Sunday 30th March 1851.
xxi	In churches with more than one service it is not possible to assess the total attendance because the clergy were not asked to stipulate how many attended more than one.
xxii	From Watton's Newpaper Cuttings ref. SA/C/ 04/f. This newspaper cutting was written in the fulsome language of the time beginning with the words 'The inhabitants of the village and parish of Shinton – so picturesquely situated on the south of the Severn, which here winds its serpentine course through a most delightful valley, bounded on the north side by the richly diversified rising ground which is crowned by the heights of the far-famed Wrecking, and on the other confined by the bold ridge of hill country, known as Winlock Hedge – were, on Thursday last, once again summoned by the pealing of the bells of the church of St Peter and St Paul, to worship in the edifice where their forefathers had for ages knelt, and which had of late gone into such a dilapidated condition that the work of restoration or substitution became imperatively necessary.' The Revd George Burd was instrumental in the rebuilding of Cressage Church in 1840.
xxiii	The new rectory is absent from the 1841 Tithe Map but is in the railway route plan of 1846 so must have predated the church restoration.

xxiv   Lee family members included Henry Phillips Lee, vicar of Cressage 1923-34. He married Harriet Jane Danks, the artist who painted Sheinton Church and its Rectory. A descendant of the family, Mrs Helen Lanning, kindly supplied the two paintings by Harriet Jane Danks.

xxv   Since the 1854 restoration minor internal changes had been made but no major restoration of the fabric was begun till 2001 under the leadership of an enthusiastic churchwarden.

THE MANOR AND LANDOWNERS FROM THE 16TH TO 18TH CENTURIES

Trevor G Hill

In 1772 Robert Williams, the rector of Sheinton, sent a return to the bishop in which he said *'The parish of Sheinton is very small and not more than a mile across and less in some parts; it contains no village or hamlet and contains only twenty-seven houses. There are no families of note in it, the inhabitants being all farmers and cottagers; twenty-five of the former and two of the latter.'* Williams was making a comment on the fact that Sheinton, unlike Acton Burnell or Cound, did not contain a castle, mansion or large gentry house. That is not to say the gentry had no influence on the parish, for Sheinton had been held by a lord of the manor since Saxon times. From deeds and similar records it has been possible to discover some of the gentry families who had an influence on the residents of Sheinton.[1]

The Lordship and Manor House of Sheinton

As has been noted in Chapter 4 the manor of Sheinton had been held by several lords with names such as Hugh de Sheinton but by 1423 a surname had been adopted for in that year we find Hugh Harnage of Sheinton as a witness of a settlement indenture.[ii] It was from a study of the deeds relating to Sheinton manorial lordship that the existence of a manor house began to emerge. The first evidence was a deed of 1661[iii] in which Humphrey Harnage of Sheinton Esq agreed with Richard Harnage, yeoman of the Coles, Broseley over the discharge of his debts. The document refers to *'the manor house or hall where Humphrey Harnage lives and appurtenances and grounds…for the use of Humphrey Harnage for life; and then to Mrs Katherine Harnage; his sister for life; then to Richard Harnage…'*(figure 8.1).

Figure 8.1 The Harnage deed of 1661 (courtesy of Shropshire Archives, Moseley Collection 2089/1/41)

The Harnage pedigree indicates that Katherine was buried in Sheinton 1670 while her sister, Thomasin, had been buried earlier, in 1658.[iv]

On 1st August 1663 there is confirmation that Humphrey was also lord of the manor. Humphrey leased to Richard Harnage *'the main manor house and lordship of Sheinton all that said manor and premises from the date thereof for four score and nineteen years...'* [v] He was buried in Sheinton on 14th August 1663.[vi] The Harnage family pedigree created by the antiquarians Joseph and George Morris indicates that Humphrey had married Eleanor, and she appears in the Hearth Tax of Sheinton in 1672 as a widow living in a house with two hearths.[vii] The genealogies further suggest that Humphrey Harnage was born in 1623 the son of Richard Harnage and Audrey (nee Humphrey) and trace the association with Sheinton back for a further three generations to a Richard Harnage of Sheinton who married firstly Dorothy Scriven and secondly Jane Kynaston (nee Oteley). This Richard was assessed for £9 – 1 – 0 in the Lay Subsidy of 1525;[viii] he was the son of Hugh Harnage the lessee of the Belswardine estate and Margaret (nee Lacon). This Hugh was a descendant of Hugh Harnage of Sheinton mentioned above whose son William is recorded as the first lessee of the Belswardine estate.

The name of Edward Harnage associated with land in Sheinton also appears in deeds dated between 1624 and 1639.[ix] It is assumed that he was one of the Edward Harnages of Belswardine and therefore a later relative of Hugh Harnage. Further, the relationship between Humphrey Harnage and Richard Harnage of Broseley who paid off his debts is uncertain but again he appears to be a relative. This Richard does not appear in the Morris pedigrees, which suggests that they only recorded families from the higher echelons of society rather than their relations who were *'in trade'*. Richard Harnage of the Coles, Broseley was recorded in 1661 and 1663 as a yeoman and from a lease granted in 1671 as a trowman.[x] His son William, who appears in deeds from 1690, was recorded as a waterman of the city of Bristol. Evidence of Richard's involvement in trading activity is amplified by the covenant in the deed of 1661 which states that he would supply *'four tons of coal and one ton of slack to the Town Meadow, Sheinton yearly during the life of the Humphrey Harnage'*. From the Gloucester Port Books database we also learn that William's elder brother Nabaoth, who was baptised in Broseley in 1649, was both a merchant and owned boats on the River Severn.[xi] From the port books we get snippets of data which help us understand his involvement in trade. Nabaoth Harnage is listed making a journey with his boat called the *Thomas of Shrewsbury* carrying iron and timber from Gloucester to Bristol in 1674. He is also listed in 1693 with his boat the *Ann of Broseley* carrying coal, tin, earthenware and Spanish wine from Bristol to Gloucester. It is clear therefore that this branch of the family was associated both with river trade on the Severn and the industry of Broseley.

On the death of Humphrey the Sheinton property and lordship of the manor passed to Richard of Broseley and then to his son, William Harnage, a waterman of Bristol. In 1690 William Harnage sold the lordship and property of Sheinton manor to Philip Benthall and from a later abstract of title dated 1781 it is possible to trace the subsequent history of Sheinton manor. By 1721 the manor had been inherited by Edward Browne as heir-at-law of Philip Benthall who sold it to Samuel Littlehales.[xii] Various deeds from 1721 relating to the Littlehales family tell us more about the state of the property:

'And also one piece or parcel of land situate, lying and being in Sheinton aforesaid and commonly called or known by the name of the Hall Yard and whereon one capital messuage formerly stood and now only part thereof is standing, and also one piece or parcel of land etc known as Bowling Green and formerly adjoining to but now lying together with the Hall Yard… containing by estimation seven acres'.

Therefore although the manor title and land were now in the hands of the Littlehales family it is clear that the manor house was in a poor state of repair (figure 8.2).

Figure 8.2 An artist's impression of Sheinton Manor House (drawn by Amanda C Hill, 2006)

By 1725 the house had finally disappeared for a deed between Samuel Littlehales, mercer of Much Wenlock and Richard Littlehales of Bridgnorth, gent, states:

'All that manor or reputed manor of Sheinton and one parcel called Hall Yard where a capital messuage formerly stood, and now no part thereof is standing; and the Bowling Green about 7 acres now or late Samuel Munslow, John Clark, Charles Davies, Joseph Holmes, Richard Skett, Henry Powell, Matthew Nock, Richard Nock the Elder, Abraham Davies, Richard Nock, Thomas Binner, Elizabeth Binner widow, Joan Evans widow, Dorothy Davies, Edward Yardley, John Shaw, Margaret Portsman, William Morgan.'

In 1806 Walter Michael Moseley of Glasshampton, Worcs purchased the Manor and manorial title from John Littlehales of Winchester, a descendant of Samuel Littlehales. The deed for this transfer again confirms that the manor house was no longer standing with the words *'The manor or reputed manor of Sheynton and the Hall Yard whereon one capital messuage formerly stood and the Bowling Green now lying together with the Hall Yard…'* By 1807 an enclosure agreement also shows that Walter Michael Moseley held the title 'Lord of the manor of Sheinton'. In figure 8.3 the area of Hall Yard is identified as a prime position in the centre of the village next to the parish church and may have been a site that was occupied as far back as the Romano-British period (see figure 5.1).

Figure 8.3 The area of Hall Yard(16) on 1808 map (courtesy of Shropshire Archives, Moseley Collection 2089/5/2/34-5)

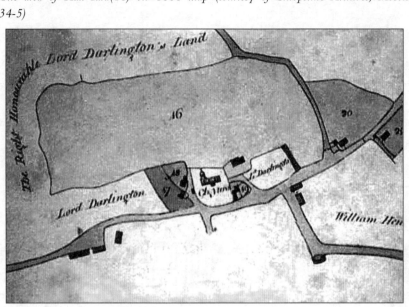

The Shinewood Estate

A manor survey and map of 1747 does not include any reference to the Shinewood estate and as is noted in Chapter 4 it appears to have been a freehold estate since the time of Domesday. It has been suggested by Christopher Andrea in his book on the Shinewood Mill that in the 15th century it belonged to Wenlock Abbey but this is unlikely.[xiii] The estate appears to have been created from two areas of land known as Shinewood and Jackstocking.[xiv] A note in Henry Woodd's book of 1886 says that Jackstocking *'is an adjacent property and once belonged to Shinewood. It is on the left side of the high road from Wenlock'*.[xv]

From the 16th century details of the families that lived at Shinewood can be established. In about the year 1510 Alexander Woodd, the third son of Lawrence Woodd of Holly Hall, Yorkshire who had already established a Shropshire connection when he married Joanna Yonge the daughter and heiress of Sir William Yonge of Caynton, settled at Shinewood and held the estate under a lease.[xvi] The Woodd family pedigree, deeds and other records show that they occupied a number of estates in Shropshire that included Shinewood, White Abbey (sometimes recorded as Black Abbey) in Alberbury, and West Coppice.

According to the family pedigree Alexander Woodd married Joan Haycock and they had four sons and one daughter. Further it states that Alexander Woodd was living in Shinewood before 1525 and was there until at least 1543-4. A footnote comments that Blakeway considered that he was the bailiff of Buildwas abbey after the dissolution (1535-6), and also that Peter Woodd was tenant of Oldfield, Sheinton. In 1526 Alexander Woodd's

Sheinton estate was valued as £8-1-0 and taxed at 4 shillings.[xvii] His will of 1546, records him as of Shinewood and White Abbey and stated that he wished to be buried in the chancel of Alberbury Church *'where my fyrst wife was buried'* and also that *'I give to the reparac'ons of the Churche of Shenton tenne shyllinges'*. . . [xviii]

The estate of Shinewood and Jackstocking was inherited by Peter Woodd who held the estate from before 1544 and until 1571-2. His will, dated 1567 and proved in London April 1575, shows his attachment to Shinewood and to Sheinton church when he writes:

'I Peter Woodd of Jackstocking in the parish of Sheinton… my bodie to be buried in the Parrishe Churche of Shenton in myne owne forme betwixt my father and the wall. Also my will is that my wife Felia Woode shall have my house at Jackstocking with all the grounde that belongeth therunto during the yeres of my lease (if she so longe doe live) the Mille and Farme house with all other my lease and leases and all other my chattels as well reall as p'sonall duringe the yeres I have in them…and after her decease My will is that my said children Will'm Henry Thomas Edward and Richard or so manye of them as be alive shall have for their keepinge and mainten'nce my sayd house in Jackstocking the Mille and Farme house with all the grounde belonging to the said house with all other my lease and chattels both reall personall duringe the tyme an so long as the said Will'm Henry Thomas Edward and Richard my children shall be unmarried and not placed in their owne . . .'[xix]

There follow further details of the son's inheritance, a list of other beneficiaries and the signatures of two of his sons, Richard Woodd, Henry Woodd and his wife Felys (Felicia) Wood. Peter Wood and Felicia (nee Warham) had six sons and one daughter. Alexander (2) and Henry also married twice while the other four sons, William, Edward, Thomas and Richard died without issue. Peter's only daughter Joan died prior to 1567, the date of his will. Peter Wood was described as of Shinewood and White Abbey, Alberbury, although he appears to have also lived at Boreatton, Baschurch and Alberbury. It is noted from other records that annual payments were made by the Shinewood mill owners or occupiers to the Harnage family for use of water from this brook.[xx]

Alexander Wood (2) married Elizabeth Onslow by whom he had three daughters. His second marriage was to Elizabeth Jennings when they had two sons and three daughters. He had inherited the Shinewood and Alberbury estates but we do not know if he ever lived at Shinewood. Both of his wives were buried at Alberbury and two of his daughters were baptised there. Alexander's eldest son Peter Wood (2) (c.1578 - 1658) inherited the title *'as of Shinewood and Alberbury'* but Alberbury appears to have become the principal family seat for all his children were baptised there. However, the estate of Shinewood may have continued as a family home until at least 1672 when Mrs Mary Wood the widow of Peter Wood (2) is listed for Hearth Tax on 8 hearths in Sheinton and paid 16s.[xxi]

In another deed Peter Wood (3) is also described as *'of Shinewood'*, and he died in August 1667. His will was proved on 21st August at Lichfield and his probate inventory dated 9th August 1667 lists his property at Shinewood and shows that three members of the family, Edward, Basil and Frances acted as witnesses to the four appraisers who were John Adams, Roger Nock, Edward Harries and Richard Hennecocks. They estimated the total value of his moveable goods as £108 - 11 - 0 which indicates that he was a man of some substance: £1 in 1667 being roughly equivalent to £60 in 1992 (thus = to £6,500). [xxii] Among his household goods there were a silver cup and eight silver spoons worth £1, pewter ware, including fourteen pewter dishes worth £2, and four feather beds with their blankets and coverings valued at £6. He had a new saddle and a *crapper* (crupper) for his horses, an old mare and a two-year old colt worth £3. He had a breastplate and one case of pistols and we know that the Woodd family had supported the Royalist cause in the Civil War.[xxiii]

At his death Peter (3) was farming the Shinewood estate. It was a mixed farm with arable fields growing muncorn, barley, oats and peas.[xxiv] Some of the muncorn was in the barn and about 50 thraves still in the field. The standard thrave was *'two stooks of twelve sheaves'* so there may have been 1200 sheaves of corn awaiting transport to the barn. Peter also had hay in the barn worth £10 and various farm tackle worth £4 – 7 – 0. He also had animals: four oxen which would have been used for ploughing, nine cows in milk with one barren cow, two heifers, five yearlings and five calves. He had a flock of sixteen sheep and some pigs and poultry. It appears that the mill was not functioning for it was being used as a store and may have also been used as the dairy for the items listed suggest cheese or butter making – *'barrel stands, milk tubbs, a churn, pails and other treen ware'*, the latter term referring to items made of wood used in a dairy.

Although no deeds have yet been discovered to establish the changeover of ownership or occupancy of the Shinewood estate, an indenture for a poor boy, John Binner, in 1692 states he was apprenticed to Thomas Lea, a yeoman farmer of Shinewood. [xxv] By 1725 the estate appears to have passed into the hands of the Hassall family and the Sheinton parish register records the burials of Mr Thomas Hassall and members of his family.[xxvi]

By 1771 the Shinewood estate was owned by Hugford Hassall and he leased the Shinewood and Jackstocking estate to William Corfield of Harley. The deed states that the estate included Shinewood Farm of 180 acres which was in the tenancy of William Adams and Thomas Harriman. Later William Corfield purchased the estate and bequeathed it to his daughter Sarah who had married Thomas Evans on 17th April 1773.[xxvii] Under William Corfield's will dated 29 June 1779, Thomas Evans and his wife Sarah inherited the estate of Shinewood. When Thomas Evans died in 1794 the estate was conveyed the next year to his wife who died in 1806. It appears that she had lived at Shinewood, with her son Thomas Evans (2) who continued to hold the estate until 1847 as is indicated by his will of 14 Dec 1847. The Shinewood estate eventually became absorbed into the Moseley's estate of Buildwas Park and was included with other land in Sheinton in the sale of this estate in 1928/29. [xxviii] Figure 8.4 shows the house at Shinewood. The construction has been dated to the late 18th century and it was probably built when the Corfield family owned the estate.

Figure 8.4 Shinewood House from the 1929 sale catalogue (courtesy of Mrs Faith Davies)

CONCLUSION

It is clear from this chapter that whilst Robert Williams the rector in 1772 stated that '*There are no families of note in Sheinton*' that this did not mean there was no gentry influence in the parish.

REFERENCES

i   The term 'Deed' is used here for a wide range of documents such as marriage settlements, leases, lease & release documents, mortgages & indentures. Wills, rentals, surveys, letters and solicitors' opinions, helpful in determining land ownership or occupation, are also available for Sheinton, many as original documents, copies, or details in later abstracts which list earlier transactions. Much of this chapter has been culled from these documents.

ii   A Settlement Indenture of the Wolryche family of Bridgnorth, 19th August 1423, SA 2922/3/4.

iii   A feoffment – Moseley Collection Deeds, SA 2089/1/4/1.

iv   Morris, J, Shropshire Genealogy, Mic 150 6001/4078, p660 and George Morris, Shropshire Genealogy, Mic 147, Vol IV, p434.

v   What later becomes known as a 99-year lease. Moseley Collection Deeds SA 2089/1/4/2.

vi   Phillimore, W P W, gen ed, *Shropshire Parish Registers,* Vol II – Sheinton, Shropshire Parish Register Society, 1901, p27. Sheinton parish registers before 1711 were lost and the early entries were compiled by extracting details from George Morris. See note iv above.

vii   Watkins-Pritchard, W, *Shropshire Hearth Tax 1672,* Shropshire Archaeological and Parish Register Society, Shrewsbury, 1949.

viii   Faraday, M A, *Lay Subsidy of Shropshire 1524-7,* University of Keele, Shropshire Record Series, 1999

ix   SA Deeds 6001/6 Vol 3 p60, & 6001/6 Vol 3 p62.

x   Moseley Collection Deeds SA Deeds 2089/1/4/1, 2089/1/4/2 & 2089/1/7/29. Much of what follows about the Harnages is drawn from this collection.

xi   Broseley Parish Register & Gloucester Port Book Database, 1575 - 1765, on CD ROM, Adam Matthew Publications & University of Wolverhampton. Reference nos. 1249/10/06/13 & 1252/03/10/09.

xii   Moseley Collection Deeds SA 2089/1/4/21.

xiii   Andrea, C, 'Historical and Structural history of Sheinwood Mill, Shropshire,' unpublished thesis, Ironbridge Institute, 1990, p5. His argument for the mill is based on this misquote: *'Walter de Clifforde… gave to the sustenance of the kitchen of the monks [of Wenlock]… the mill of Cineton, with a messuage belonging to the mill…'.* However, a check of the *Valor Ecclesiasticus* showed it was not listed among the holdings of Wenlock Priory, or any other abbey(SA. C96-571). This suggests that by the time of the dissolution it had passed back into lay hands. It had probably been held by Haughmond Abbey for it depends upon how one reads the translation of the cartulary of Haughmond Abbey by Revd M A Leighton TSAS, Vol 1, (1878 p176). He writes *'Walter de Clifford, the son of Walter de Clifford, gave to the sustenance of the kitchen of the monks and their refections in fresh fish, the mill of Cineton (Shineton near Much Wenlock, co Salop), and half a virgate of land in Shineton, with a messuage belonging to the mill of Shineton, and suit of service.'.* No date can be attributed to this gift and further there is no guarantee that the mill mentioned was the one at Shinewood as there were others in the parish.

xiv   In Mumford W F, *Wenlock in the Middle Ages,* 1977, p105 there is mention of a William Bayley of the Stockinge, gent c1595. Is there any connection of this with Jackstocking? According to Foxall, H D G, *Shropshire Field names,* 1980, Jack when applied to a field could mean vacant or unused land, land for which no ownership was claimed. As Stocking also means land cleared of trees it is suggested that originally this was a piece of woodland that had been cleared and was absorbed into the Shinewood estate. No field names so far indicate where it was.

xv   Note that this branch of the Wood family spelt their name with two d's and their descendants in New Zealand still follow this spelling. Woodd, Henry, *The Family of Woodd,* 1886 (SA BW 87). Except for actual quotes, the name is standardised as Wood. This document has been used extensively in what follows.

xvi   The lease has not been discovered but it was noted in the will of Peter Wood 1567.

xvii   Faraday, M A, *Lay Subsidy of Shropshire*

xviii   Woodd, H, *op cit,* pp60-61.

xix   Woodd, H, *op cit,* pp59-60.

xx   For example Moseley Collection Deeds SA 2089/1/4/25-26 dated 1771.

xxi   Watkins-Pritchard, W, *Shropshire Hearth Tax 1672,* Shropshire Archaeological and Parish Register Society, Shrewsbury, 1949.

xxii   Based upon the Bank of England's Equivalent contemporary values of the pound; historical series 1270 - 1992 in Munby, L, *How much is that worth?* British Association for Local History, second edition, 1996, pp38-39.

xxiii   Peter's uncle, Basil Wood (1) Chancellor of St Asaphs 1605 & of Rochester 1618 suffered for his Royalist devotion. Salisbury, E R G, *Border County Worthies,* Oswestry Advertiser Office, 1878, & *Alumni Oxeniensis 1500 – 1714,* Parker & Co, 1892.

xxiv   Muncorn: mixture of wheat and rye sown together.

xxv   SA MI 258/1 & Phillimore, W P W, gen ed, *Shropshire Parish Registers,* Vol II – Sheinton, Shropshire Parish Register Society, 1901, pp10&16.

xxvi   Sheinton Parish registers record burials of: Augustine son of Mr Thomas Hassall, 8 Apr 1741; Ann daughter of Mr Thomas Hassall, 2 May 1741; Mr Thomas Hassall, 10 May 1741 & Sarah Hassall 12 Feb 1761.

xxvii   Thomas Evans, baptised at Leighton, 23rd Oct 1743, but described as of Belswardine.

xxviii   Lane Saville & Co, with Barber & Son, Sale Catalogue of the Buildwas Estate, 1928 & 1929. Loaned to the author by Mrs F. Davies; copies held at SA 690/9.

9

A Glimpse of Sheinton School

Norman Davies

Background

Although it was not compulsory for parishes to provide schools until the passing of the Education Act of 1870, when attendance was made compulsory for children under ten, Sheinton National School (Mixed) with residence for a Head Mistress attached was built in 1845 for 50 children (figure 9.1).

Figure 9.1 Sheinton school in the early 1900's (courtesy of Sheinton Churchwardens)

During the second half of the nineteenth century a number of laws concerning education were passed. In 1862 a Revised Code was issued as the basis for the development of education for the next forty years. To be eligible for a state grant a school had to bring forward a certain number of pupils able to pass examinations carried out by inspectors. Many saw this concentration on basics, the system of 'payment by results,' as destroying much of the progress made in previous decades.

One of the few good features of the Revised Code of 1862 was the requirement of Head Teachers to keep a diary or logbook detailing what was happening in schools and in particular commenting on attendance levels and visitors. These log books can aid the understanding not only of the education system but also of town and village society right into the twentieth century.

From 1862 schools supposedly had to be inspected annually but Sheinton School was not inspected until 1874. The Inspector of schools had *visited* in 1870 but the then headmistress Fanny R Cooper was not a certificated teacher and it was not until October 1874 that she was awarded the certificate. The report states that the grant for the school could begin to run from November 1874 with a further inspection in April 1875. This also meant that the school now had to keep a logbook. Fanny's first entry in the logbook (November 2nd 1874) reads: 'H.M. Inspector Temple gave me my certificate and said I was to commence in the code register and keep a logbook from this date.'

The Education Act of 1902 made County Council and County Borough Councils the local authorities for technical, secondary and, with a few exceptions, elementary schools. The County Council sent enquiry forms to each school asking questions on the date of the building, size of classrooms, teachers' qualifications and salaries, curriculum taught, income and expenditure.

Extracts from the report on Sheinton School 1902

Parishes from where the children come to school
Sheinton, Buildwas, Belswardine and Leighton

Premises
Erected in 1845. Total area 336 Square Yards.

Schoolroom	Length	Breadth	Height (In Feet)
Main Room	24	12	12.4.
Classroom	10	12	12.4.

32 Children on Books
Teacher's Dwelling House
School Mistress, Husband and family
Owner – Conveyed to Trustees.
Insured by Salop Fire Office for £110

Curriculum
Seniors: English, as understood, Reading, Writing, Recitation, Composition, Arithmetic, Drawing (Boys), Needlework (Girls), Object Lessons, Geography, History, Singing, and Physical Drill.
Infants: Reading, Writing, Numbers, Simple lessons on Common Things, Drawing (Boys), Needlework (Girls), Singing and P.E.

Terms of Head Teacher
£40 per Annum with increases according to the state of school funds. Paid quarterly. House and coal supplied, taxes paid. Mistress engaged to teach in Sunday school and preside over the singing of the children in Church.

Managers
Henry Lee, Sheinton Rectory, Chairman and Treasurer.
C. Maud, Archdeacon of Salop, Swan Hill, Shrewsbury.
T.B. Goucher, Sheinton.

Who were the managers?

Before the education act of 1870 many schools were built and funded by the local gentry. There is, however, no record of Sheinton School until the first logbook of 1874. At the time it was built William L Childe was Lord of the Manor with the Duke of Cleveland

and Walter Moseley Esq, joint landowners of the parish. The local Vicar was usually on the management committee and also took an active part in running the school. The second entry in the logbook is dated November 9th 1874: *'Rev Wayne heard class 1 read'*. Other similar entries include:

December 4th 1877 *'Elder children visited Birmingham cattle market. Treated by Rev Wayne'*;
May 28th 1878 *'Rev & Mrs Wayne & family left Sheinton'*;
July 16th *'Rev H Lee & Mrs Lee visited school'*;
Oct 10th *'Tea at Rectory given by Rev & Mrs Lee'*.

Throughout the history of the school there are many entries in the logbooks of parties being held at the Rectory and also at Buildwas Park.

Grant Aid

In order to supplement local support effectively the most obvious way for managers to acquire grants was from the annual inspection. To qualify for grants additional expenditure was often necessary to meet standards of accommodation and efficiency. Final expenditure was carefully scrutinised and details published on the school door for all to see. Unless managers complied with the requirements of the report the grant could be withheld.

The report for May 1875: 'This little school is in excellent order and is taught with much spirit. The reading is unusually good. Greater variety of arithmetic should be practised in lower classes. The elder scholars have been taught to understand thoroughly whatever they have read and learned'.

However, not all reports were good. April 1892: 'There is no urinal for boys; both sexes have to use the same closet. The management has been warned that the grant will be withheld if the school does not become more efficient'. It appears that the warning was not heeded, for we read in the 1894 report 'I have to state that unless the premises have been satisfactorily reconstructed during the current school year my lords will have to withhold the next grant'. And in 1895: 'Toilets still not up to standard. They are too near the school and smell offensively. No grant will be paid under article 105 of the code'.

Until 1897 the reports were all unsatisfactory but a report in the logbook for November 11th that year reads 'School closed for alterations'. It was reopened on December 6th.

In 1901, 'The children are dealt with in a kindly manner and the mistress does her best to improve their attainments. The elder boys attend irregularly during the latter part of the year. No grant is payable under section 10j article of the code since H M Inspector is unable to report that the staff is efficient or the school is well taught under the meaning of the article'.

School attendance

Another problem was the irregularity of attendance, since a minimum of 176 days a year was required of each pupil after 1862 for enlistment on the examination schedule. A problem for managers was the size of the school. Sheinton had only 16 scholars on average in 1891 and even if all passed successfully only a very modest grant could be earned. No wonder the managers had difficulty in paying for the upkeep of the premises – the amount of grant for that year was just £13. By 1895 the average attendance rose to 27 but by 1901 had fallen to 21. Although the school was built to accommodate 50 pupils it never reached this figure, the highest recorded being 43 in February 1941 due to the influx of evacuees. When the school closed in 1957 there were just 7 on the register. Reasons for absence recorded in the logbooks are many and varied:

Weather

December 7th 1874 'Very few children in school this week due to snow and frost. Walking is very dangerous'.

November 10th 1876 'Poor attendance due to much rain which makes the roads too dirty for the little ones who live some distance away to attend'.

Every winter there are many entries regarding problems with the weather, especially in the winter of 1947 when the number of pupils on the books was 21.

Reports for the 27th, 28th, 29th and 30th January say 'Heavy snowfall and bitterly cold. Only 5 children present'.

From February 4th until the 10th: 'attendances disregarded owing to weather'.

And again on March 5th, 6th and 7th: 'No scholars, roads blocked with enormous drifts'.

On July 12th 1927: 'School abandoned due to heavy thunder storm'.

Illness

Poor health was the cause of many low attendances and the closure of the school in times of epidemics.

June 17th 1879 'Many children away with severe colds'.

July 9th 1883 'School closed for 1 week, Measles and Whooping cough'.

March 7th-21st 1887 'Closed due to epidemic of Measles'.

Indeed the school report for 1887 reads 'Advised that the report is at a disadvantage due to the recent measles epidemic'.

The entry of April 29th 1937 refers to children of my mother's sister: 'Marjorie Halford has measles, Muriel, Douglas and Doreen Halford absent as contact cases. Dr Weston advised to close the school to prevent any further outbreak of measles'. During this epidemic 138 attendances were lost.

Teaching

A certain standard was required for the annual inspection and was recorded in the Inspector's report as in 1880: 'Would like to see better results. Discipline good. Writing and spelling could improve. Arithmetic very weak. Geography not satisfactory. Religious education very good'.

And in 1893, 'Exams point to an inefficient school, many improvements needed in all subjects. There will be no grant payable under rule 105'.

Things did improve slightly as more efficient teaching material was requested in this report. Two new desks were delivered with eight pictures for object lessons, colour charts, drawing charts, one dozen lead pencils, one dozen rulers, one dozen India rubbers, eight Century Historical readers, geographical readers std. 3&4, English grammar books, Arithmetic books, four dozen copy books, box of pens, slate pencils and one dozen slates. It was not until 1932 that the school received a top class report. 'This small rural school is effectively conducted. Individual work is judiciously conducted with group teaching and all children reach a creditable level in most subjects. English is taught on secondary lines and attempts to develop *literary lines have achieved some successes'.*

The number on the register at this time was 36. The teacher was Miss Zillah Hughes who left in 1947 for Harley school.

Head Teachers 1874-1957

There are no records of Sheinton School before 1874; however, the 1851 census returns show that Harriet Hamilton aged 45 and unmarried was employed as a National School Mistress.

1874-1892	Fanny Rachel Cooper
1892-1912	S. A. Morris
1912-1917	Mary Elizabeth Hall
1917-1919	Emily Elizabeth Evans
1919-1923	Edith Maud Hancock
1923-1927	Gladys Mary Davies
1927-1929	Annie Mycock
1929-1947	Zillah Hughes
1947-1950	Enid Jones
1950-1957	Isabel Henderson

Closure

The school finally closed in 1957, colour photo 9.1, (centre section).

The last entry in the logbook is dated April 12th 1957: *'This school will be discontinued from the end of this afternoon's session. The children will be transferred to Cressage School. I Isabel J Henderson relinquish the post of Headmistress of this school as from April 29th 1957.'*

This has been only a glimpse into the records in these logbooks but it can be seen over the 83 years history of the school what changes took place, especially the introduction of better health and sanitary facilities, as shown in HMI reports on toilets and later on temperature, ventilation and light. From the early 20th century Doctors, Nurses and Dentists visited the school regularly but epidemics of illness such as measles and influenza still occurred. Although many of the children were admitted to school at an early age, complaints about pupils' irregular attendance and the indifference of some parents were common, even if these complaints were louder in larger schools such as Much Wenlock. The physical effort to walk long distances from home to school and return — some would live up to two miles away - was an endurance especially for those in poor health after epidemics and during winter months. The meagre diet of poor families, at its worst in winter, resulted in many children having little resistance to illness. This is a reflection of the social conditions prevalent in small towns and villages over 100 years ago.

Why write about Sheinton School?

The village of Sheinton holds many family connections and lots of childhood memories for me. My mother, Mrs Connie Davies, nee Connie Wall, was born here as was my

Grandfather Richard Henry Wall (born 1879) and my Great Grandfather George Wall (born 1840). My grandfather, mother, her two sisters, four brothers and cousins who lived in the village were all educated at the school.

At the age of 14 my mother won a Shropshire-wide essay competition and was presented with a medal by the Lord Lieutenant of Shropshire at the West Midland Show. But circumstances meant that she never had the opportunity to progress beyond what she called 'Sheinton Grammar'.

REFERENCES

Birchenough, C, *History of Elementary Education in England and Wales 1800-1938*, Universal Tutorial Press, 1938

Manager's returns under 1902 Education Act, Sheinton C of E School, Shropshire Archives

Sheinton School Log Books 1874-1957, Shropshire Archives

10
FARMERS, SMALLHOLDERS COTTAGERS AND THEIR FAMILIES

Margaret A Hill

From the 18th century we can begin to build a picture of the lives of ordinary men and women using the records kept in the parish by the church and the overseers of the poor. By the 19th century the historical sources available include the Tithe Records, Trade Directories, Railway records, Census Enumerator Books and School Records.

People in Parish Registers

The parish of Sheinton can be viewed from many viewpoints but one of the most interesting is to consider the people who have made Sheinton their home over the centuries. Although a few of their names can be discovered on tombstones in the churchyard, the most rewarding sources are the record of Baptisms, Marriages and Burials in the Parish Registers and the census returns from 1841 to 1901. Parish Registers were kept from 1538 but unfortunately those for Sheinton have only survived after 1712. Before then names can be gleaned from wills and probate inventories, from deeds and marriage settlements and also from church records known as Glebe Terriers which are a record of the land and property held by the vicar.

In Sheinton we also have a valuable window into the parish in 1747 with the estate map of Lord Newport which was drawn by John Rocque.[1] The survey book which goes with the map names all the tenants of his lordship at that date. This is a valuable additional source because although the parish registers cover a long period of time they are an ecclesiastical record which was not made with local historians in mind. Many individuals lived in the parish without any record of their name appearing in the parish register so without alternative documentation their presence would go unnoticed.

To enable these church-orientated parish registers to reveal the life histories of the parishioners of Sheinton it has been necessary to reconstitute the members of each nuclear family. This has been done by making an index-card for each family on which parents and children are listed, together with the particular events and the dates on which they occurred.[ii] From this index it has been possible to find some indication of family size, the age at marriage and the age at burial for periods when this information was not included. There is a common belief that the size of families in the past, especially in the 19th century, was much larger than at the present day. Although in some cases this may be true it cannot be assumed to be universal. Several factors affect the number of children a wife could bear, one of the most significant being the age at marriage. Apart from local and family custom the age at which a couple were free to marry was subject to several constraints: having a sufficient income to support a family; being freed from the rules imposed by apprenticeship which forbade marriage until it had been completed; and being able to find accommodation in which to set up their new home. The contrast between young men employed in industry (i.e. the coal-field) and those who worked in agriculture is very distinct.[iii] By the age of eighteen industrial workers were earning a man's wage which would enable them to marry, while their rural counterparts were probably working on the family farm for not much more than their bed and board. This meant that the former would marry young and raise a larger family than the farmer's son who in extreme circumstances might have to wait until he took over the farm in his own right.

In the past the frequency of conception was dependant on the length of time a mother continued to breast-feed her baby. This usually resulted in a pregnancy about every two years or so, though if a baby died in infancy the period would be shorter. Families who could afford a wet-nurse for their child lost this contraceptive advantage and so for many gentlewomen childbirth became an annual event. Elizabeth the wife of Rev William Dicken baptised three children in the first three years of their marriage while the next four births were two years apart and the last two of her nine children three years apart.[iv] Was she unable to afford a wet-nurse or had she come to realise the value of natural contraception?

The baptism registers between 1712 and 1850 reveal that over this long period of time only seven families had large families while the majority had only between one and three children (figure 10.1).

Figure 10.1 Family Size in Sheinton 1712 to 1850 ex Family Reconstitution (Margaret A Hill)

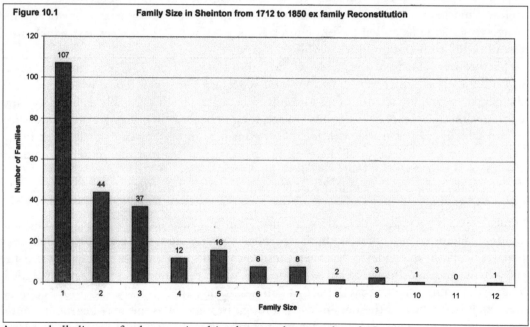

As we shall discuss further on in this chapter the people of Sheinton comprised a very mobile population which resulted in many families only remaining in the parish long enough to baptise one or two children. Therefore this statistic of family size reflects the tendency of families to 'move on' rather than the low birth-rate. Another way to look at the number of children in each household is to count the children who are recorded on the census returns, but that would not take into account those who have already left home or those yet to be born.

The burial registers before 1812 do not often give the age at death but with family reconstitution when individuals have been baptised in the parish it is possible to discover this information (figure 10.2).

Figure 10.2 Age at burial of those baptised in Sheinton 1751-1850 (Margaret A Hill)

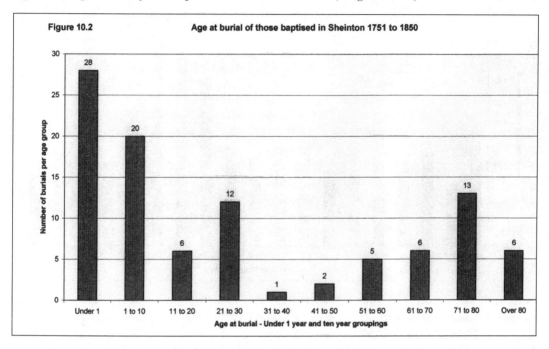

From this an idea of life expectancy can be calculated. The result is, however, weighted towards the lower age groups, especially the infants whose period between baptism and burial was very short (twenty-eight under 1 year). Although the child-mortality rate lowers the average life expectancy, there were certainly some individuals who lived to a ripe old age (seventeen between 71 and 80 and six over 80).

At certain periods of history communities have been thrown into crisis by epidemics of disease. We have heard about the Black Death, the Plague and the Victorian cholera epidemic but a lesser-known crisis event occurred around 1727-30. In a period of bad harvests when resistance to disease may have been low, a sickness known as 'relapsing fever' claimed a great many lives. Relapsing fever was so named because those infected with the disease appeared to recover but when a relapse occurred it often proved fatal. In Sheinton the annual number of burials in the early 1720's averaged about three, but in 1728 there were twelve burials none of whom were infants and only one a child. Figure 10.3 shows the effect of this outbreak in Sheinton and nine other parishes in mid-Shropshire.

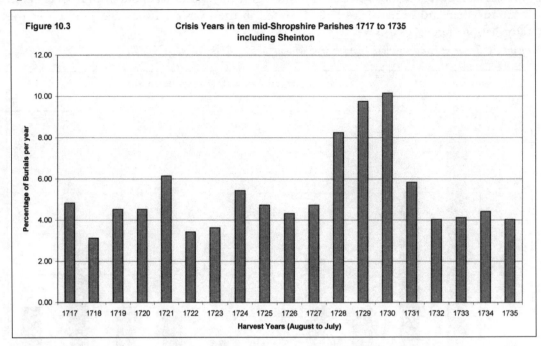

Figure 10.3 Crisis Years in ten mid-Shropshire Parishes 1717 to 1735 including Sheinton

Although starvation may have exacerbated the epidemic the upper classes were not immune from infection for the name of Mrs Mary Hugford appears among the burials. The usual childhood infections, in the absence of immunisation, often proved fatal. Sometimes the vicar may make a note of the cause of death but if not it is sometimes evident by the number of deaths, the season of the year or the family relationships of the victims. In May 1741 two of the Revd Dicken's children were buried within days of each other and in April and May Mr Thomas Hassal also lost two of his children. Hassal himself does not appear to have been immune from infection as he was buried on 10th May. As Mr Hassal's son Augustine was the first to die it seems that perhaps as visitors to the vicarage they brought the disease with them.

Sheinton families from the Census

The ten-yearly census of England and Wales was begun in 1801 with a simple count of the total population in every town and village. This continued until 1841 when the authorities felt bold enough and sufficiently organised enough to make a record of the name and approximate age and occupation of the members of each household. In this part of Shropshire we can be justly proud of William Farr who was born into a poor Kenley family and after being educated at Donnington School devised the system by which the 1841 and following censuses were organised.[vi]

From 1851 the subsequent census records were extended to include information on birthplace, health and living conditions. This was designed to enable the government to formulate its policies on a sound basis, but on a more sinister note to give some idea of the numbers of able-bodied men available for military service in the event of a future war. In the event Britain was not involved in a war in Europe until 1914 when the true health of the nation was shown to be much lower than had been imagined.

A study of the 19th century records for Sheinton has revealed that it was a small agricultural community which offered no opportunities for people to improve their situation in life.[vii] Therefore, just as in country communities today, the only alternative was to leave home in search of work. The population at any one time had to be of such a size and composition that it could be accommodated in the existing housing and employed within the local work opportunities. The only new houses were built on the common where the original squatter cottages were rebuilt in brick by the Moseleys of Buildwas Park. They purchased land in Sheinton in 1808 and by the time the estate was relinquished in 1928 there were ten holdings on the common with nine cottages.[viii] Today several of these cottages have been rebuilt into substantial houses and a few replaced by prefabricated bungalows.

The older buildings are the farmhouses, Sheinton Hall Farm and Church Farm, in the centre of the village, and Shinewood Farm, associated with Shinewood House half a mile away to the south-east. Smaller houses were at Brook Farm and the Buck to the west of Sheinton Brook, and Leech Meadow Farm, situated on a piece of rising ground near the river Severn. The last has recently been rebuilt in the centre of the village. The only houses with any style were the Rectory and Shinewood House. The Rectory was built in the 1840's on the site of the Medieval Manor House, to replace an earlier Parsonage that stood near where the schoolhouse now stands.[ix] The house at Shinewood was also a replacement for an earlier building and this itself has had later additions.

The census tells us the names of those who were sleeping in these cottages and farms on census night and their position in the household. In 1851 the largest family was the Walls with six children at home while the Dorsets, Hills, Smouts and Venables each had five children, so we can see that there was plenty of work for the midwife and later for the schoolteacher Harriet Hamilton who was born in Wellington. None of these families could afford to keep paid servants so as soon as they were old enough the children were expected to help with the daily tasks of fetching the milk, carrying the water or feeding the hens, and there was always the baby to look after. The Rector Henry Bagnell employed two servants at the Rectory but at the time of the 1851 census Shinewood House was uninhabited. For comparison we can see that ten years later Mary Pardoe (a widow) had a farm bailiff, a house servant and a groom living in the house. Sheinton Hall Farm and Church Farm both had employees living in the house, house servants and farm servants, while Charlotte Adney at Church Farm also had a bailiff to help her run the farm.

The only inn in Sheinton was the Rising Buck, now the middle cottage at The Buck on the Cressage Road. In 1851 the innkeeper was John Young who was born in Westbury and his wife came from Pulverbatch. As their three-year old son was born in Smethcott we can tell that this family are newcomers to the parish, although their next son John was baptised in Sheinton on 6th Oct 1850 and later two girls were baptised in 1852 and 1855. In 1851 no lodgers were recorded at the inn but by 1861 the railway was under construction and the inn was home to ten men who gave their occupations as railway excavators and their birthplaces as Chard, Leamington and Ireland (figure 10.4).

Figure 10.4 The Great Western Railway through Sheinton. Planned 1846, opened 1862, closed 1963 (Trevor G Hill, redrawn from Ordnance Survey maps)

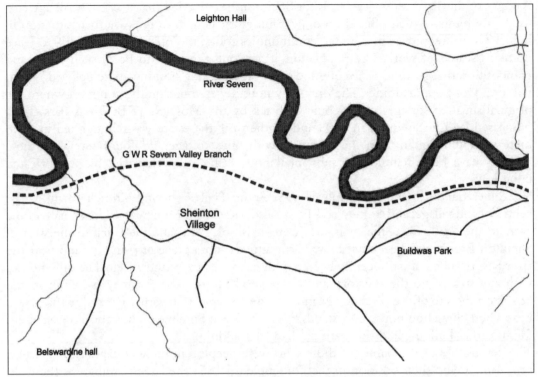

Another thirteen railway workers were living in two huts under the care of two of their wives, and three were lodging in the village with William and Elizabeth Jones and their one-year old son.

By 1861 John Young had left The Rising Buck and the new innkeeper was Margaret Barber who was baptised Margaret Tudor in Cressage on 2nd May 1822.X In 1846 she married William Barber who was described on the census as a joiner, bell-hanger and blacksmith who came from Worcester. His children were born in Longwood all except for the last, Herbert Harris Barber, who was born on 4 Nov 1859 and baptised by Rev Bailey in Sheinton Church. The two eldest girls aged twelve and ten were already 'employed at home'.

The work opportunities open to the people of Sheinton were very limited; almost all were employed on farms or worked in gardens or smallholdings and even the girls who are named as house servants might have spent some time in the dairy. John Hewlett the wheelwright and Samuel Evans the blacksmith would have been self-employed but they too would have spent their time repairing farm machinery. Although Benjamin Kite was the Parish Clerk he was also a gardener and the innkeeper kept a small farm. The shoemaker with his assistant and apprentice and John Venables, a road labourer ,are the only men whose livelihood does not depend on agriculture.

The majority of women are recorded as undertaking domestic duties and only four: the innkeeper; the schoolmistress; the keeper of the turnpike gate and one dressmaker are given any other occupation. Unlike rural villages in the East Midlands where the women made lace or straw plait at home the women of Sheinton do not appear to have any means of supplementing their income. The census was taken in late March or early April; if it had been taken during haymaking or at harvest time would the women have said they were working on the farms? The schoolmistress certainly complained that children were absent from school at harvest time.

So we can see from an analysis of the census that the opportunities in such a small parish were very limited and that it could not easily absorb a large number of young people. There is a limit to how many ten-year old bird-scarers or stone-pickers the farmers could make use of, and although the girls at The Rising Buck could be usefully employed at home, others would have to have gone to Much Wenlock or Shrewsbury to find work. However, a study of the families with several children on successive census returns shows that it was not only the young people who left to find work but whole families who migrated elsewhere. The reasons for this may have been many but we cannot but wonder whether the lack of work in so small a parish was one of them. Another factor could have been an escalation of farm and cottage rents.

Table 10.1 Occupiers of Sheinton Farms in the census years

Census	Sheinton Hall	Church Farm	Shinewood	Hilltop
1841	Andrew Dodson	Mary Adney	Thomas Evans	
1851	Andrew Dodson junr	Charlotte Adney	John Smout (Bailiff)	
1861	Sarah Dodson (wid)	Charlotte Adney	Mary Pardoe	Samuel Cadwallader
1871	Sarah Dodson (wid)	Charlotte Adney	Joseph Pardoe	Kate Ainsworth (wid)
1881	Pryce Lloyd	George Eddowes	Richard Bailey	Mary Gittens
1891	Mary Lloyd (sister)	George Eddowes	John Alvis	Frederick Yates
1901	Thomas Goucher	John Colebatch	John Alvis	Edward Jones

The tenants of Sheinton Hall Farm, Church Farm, Shinewood and Hilltop have been traced on the census between 1841 and 1901 and set out in Table 10.1 where it becomes clear that these tenancies seldom span more than two generations. The Dodson family were occupying Sheinton Hall Farm before 1841 but even here the succession from father to son and then to son's widow was very rapid. Andrew (junior) died at the age of 43 in 1858 and his widow retired from the farm before 1881 when she was about 65. She died at Albrighton in 1890 but was buried in Sheinton.

At Church Farm Mary Adney and her sister Charlotte were tenants until 1881 when they were followed by George Eddowes. By 1901 he had moved on and been replaced by John Colebatch who was already aged 76. John stayed in Sheinton until at least 1905 when his wife Sarah was buried but he himself died at Buildwas in 1911 age 86.

The farm at Shinewood had been inherited by Thomas Evans before 1807 when he is mentioned in an enclosure agreement with Henry Harnage of Belswardine and his name also appears on both the Tithe record and the 1841 census.[xi] At his burial in 1849 he was succeeded by Richard Pardoe but by the 1851 census the house was still uninhabited and John Smout appears to be acting as farm bailiff. In the following two censuses Mary and

Joseph Pardoe are at Shinewood but by 1881 Richard Bailey was in residence to be followed from 1891 by John Alvis. The 57-acre farm at Hilltop was apparently established sometime in the 1850's, maybe by the landowner who hoped to increase his rental income, and from 1861 it was farmed by several short-term tenants.

CONCLUSION

We can see therefore that a number of interesting records, now held at the Shropshire Archives, can be used to give us fascinating insights into past generations of Sheinton's inhabitants.

REFERENCES

[i]   Survey and map of the estates of John Newport by John Rocque, 1747 SA 6802

[ii]   This system is known as 'Family Reconstitution'

[iii] Based upon the author's research into families in Priorslee which was part of the parish of Shifnal

[iv]   Sheinton Parish Register

[v]   The ten parishes analysed were those of the Cressage Area Research Project

[vi]   William Farr was the superintendent of statistics at the General Register Office from 1838 to 1880 and was said to have written the Census Reports for those years. Higgs, E, *A Clearer Sense of the Census* HMSO, 1996, pp17–18

[vii] The Census Enumerator Books used in this research are housed on microfilm copies at Shropshire Archives and have been copied into Computer databases by T G Hill

[viii] SA 2089/5/2/34-35 & SA 690/9

[ix]   The last record of the parsonage being in the earlier position is the Tithe map of 1841, SA 246/1

[x]   In addition to the census records the names of clergy, farmers, innkeepers and other tradesmen appear in the Trade Directories held at Shropshire Archives: Bagshaw's 1851; Post Office 1856; Harrold's 1861; Post Office 1863; Cassey's 1871; Cassey's 1874 and Porter's 1888

[xi]   SA 2089/6/1/3

11
HOMER AND WIGWIG, LOOKING BENEATH THE SURFACE
From Early Settlement to the End of the Nineteenth Century

D S Revell

A visitor driving by the signpost to Homer and Wigwig might give an amused smile, or if intrigued, decide to take a look at settlements with such delightful names. There are two approaches. From the Much Wenlock direction you turn onto the steep, narrow, winding lane leading down the wooded slope of Wenlock Edge, which suddenly opens out onto a glorious view across the Severn Valley towards the Wrekin to the north and distant hills to the west beyond Shrewsbury, before dropping down into Homer Village. To the casual observer Homer might appear to be merely a collection of pleasant houses in an attractive setting and she might decide to move on along the lane to Wigwig. You can also approach Wigwig, so small you may miss it, from the Shrewsbury road, a cautious drive along an even narrower lane, over a ford, (unless there has been heavy rain!). But beneath the surface one can find evidence of a long and interesting history.

The Origin of Settlement: Place-name Evidence

Place-names often point to when a settlement was founded even if Wigwig and Homer are not easily explained. But place-name experts have made suggestions and old documents may contain early references though spellings changed over time and even within the same period.

Wigwig

Wigwig is an ancient settlement. The land farmed probably includes, and at least adjoins, part of the Roman villa estate of Yarchester, in Harley parish. The first firm evidence of a community in Wigwig itself is from the Anglo-Saxon period. Personal names were commonly used as the first syllable of a place-name and the name *Wicga* was well recorded in Saxon times. *Wic* can mean a dwelling[i] or dairy farm and Margaret Gelling thinks 'Wicga's dairy-farm' the most likely explanation[ii]. She has also studied the distribution of *wicham* place-names in England, noting a strong association with Romano-British settlement and roads.[iii] Dr Trevor Hill has confirmed this association in Shropshire, [iv] perhaps significant in this case with the close proximity of Yarchester Roman villa. The Tithe Apportionment of 1846[v] details field-names, and three near the south-western boundary of the Wigwig fields, two named *The Hair Chester,* and *The Upper Hair Chester,* are probably ancient, with the *chester* element being strongly associated with Roman settlement, further supporting Dr Hill's argument (1351, 1352 & 1354, figure 11.1).

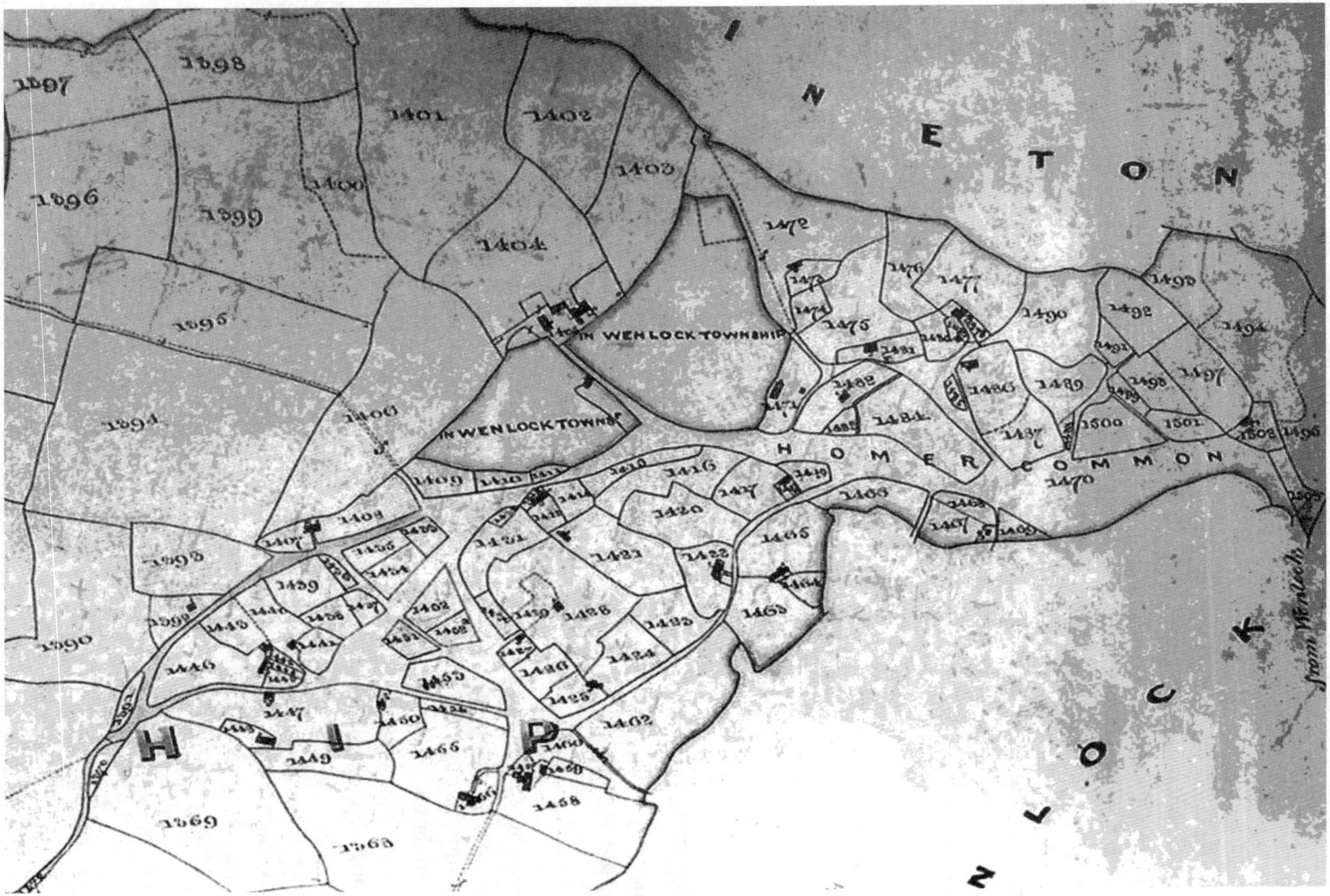

Figure 11.1 The Tithe map of Homer and Wigwig 1847(courtesy of Shropshire Archives, P198/T/1/5)

A Saxon foundation is supported by documentary evidence, as Wigwig is included in the great Domesday survey of 1086 as 'Wigewic.[vi] Other very early references include: 'Wicewica', 1121; 'Wychewyca', 1138; 'Wigewig', 1255; 'Wykwyk', 1368; 'Wigwig',1622; 'Wygwygg', 1623. Even in 1808 'Whig Whig' shows that the modern spelling had still not been established.

Homer

The land of Homer was originally included with Wigwig. Its emergence as a separate township came later, the earliest cottages most likely being built in the 16th century, with further development of squatter settlement in the 17th century on Homer Common, still called Homer Wood at that time[vii]. This was probably linked to early working of the limestone quarries in the area. The earliest references to the name appear in the 14th century, when the rivulet of 'Honemor' is mentioned in 1322 and the grove of 'Honemor' in1331.[viii] References become more common in the sixteenth century. In 1541 there was a 'Burial out of Holmere in this parish besides Wigwyk' and in 1554, a 'burial out of a Cottage or a Woodhouse within Holmere or Hollowmere.'[ix] The meaning of the name is uncertain. 'Mor' suggests 'marsh', and certainly there is poor drainage on the silty clay hillwash deposits. Water sources were vital to early settlement. Springs are to be found at the junction of the Wenlock Limestone of the Edge and the underlying impervious Wenlock Shales and several of the old cottages have shallow wells or records of them. The Oxford Names Companion states that Homer means 'a maker of helmets' and also that the first element 'Holm' is an old word for 'holly'.[x] Holly is an integral part of the semi-ancient woodland of Wenlock Edge, which gives some credence to this explanation. Margaret Gelling suggests that the first syllable may be the personal name 'Hana', or possibly derive from 'han', meaning stone, or 'hana', cock.

Whitwell

'Whitwell' means 'white spring', perhaps relating to the precipitation of calcium carbonate from the mineral-rich water issuing from underlying limestone. Certainly the spring had great local significance, perhaps renowned for healing properties as well as a water source, as it gives its name to no less than six surrounding fields and a large coppice. Whitwell Cottage is included in the outlying settlement within Much Wenlock Parish (along with Gleedon); Whitwell Mill falls within Sheinton Parish and would have been established much earlier; a cottage at Whitwell, within Wenlock Parish, appears in the 1841 Census but oddly not on the 1847 Tithe Map in the accompanying Apportionment; 'Whitwalle' was mentioned in a Rent Survey of 1550 and 'Whitwall' in 1597, both probably referring to Whitwell Mill; 'Witwell' is marked on the 1833 Ordnance Survey map with its current spelling, 'Whitwell', in the Tithe Apportionment survey of 1844–1849.

Gleedon

The name 'Gleedon' may derive from 'gleoda', meaning 'kite' and 'dun', meaning 'hill'. In the Middle Ages these birds of prey would have been common in the area, as they favour a mixed open field and woodland landscape. There is a reference to 'Le Gledenhill' in 1550; again, it is unclear whether this relates to land or the farmhouse.

Wigwig

The first firm evidence of a community at Wigwig is the Domesday survey of 1086[xi] where we are informed that Elmar held the manor of *Wigewic* in King Edward's time as a free man. It was worth fifteen shillings per annum, but following the Norman invasion in 1066 had fallen to three shillings in 1070, suggesting the land and settlements in the area were affected badly by William the Conqueror's punitive actions to submit the region to Norman rule. By 1086 Turold of Verley held the manor of Roger, Earl of Montgomery and it had made some recovery, being now worth ten shillings. There was enough land for two 'ploughs' (ox-teams, normally eight oxen apiece) which were affirmed and there were three serfs, or slaves. Also two villeins and one bordar[xii] had half a team. There may be a clerical error in the Wigwig entry as there appear to be more plough-teams than land to support them. However, in its location below Wenlock Edge there was enough woodland to fatten fifty swine.

The manor of Wigwig was given by Robert, Turold's son, to Shrewsbury Abbey in the early 12th century, initiating a period of over four hundred years of ownership by the powerful religious houses. It was passed on to Wenlock Priory before 1187 and managed as part of the priory estates (the manor of Much Wenlock), until the Dissolution.

In the Medieval period there is record of a watermill, probably close to or on the site of Mill Farmhouse. Field evidence shows traces of a former leat, taken off the Harley Brook further upstream, which ran along the upper boundary of The Slang (1379, colour photo 11.1, (centre section).

There was mention of Wigwig Mill on Harley Brook in 1291. It seems that the Mill descended with Mill Farm after the Dissolution of the Monasteries, when the Crown sold off the estates of the religious houses. In 1670 it had grown in importance, now as a fulling mill, actually two mills, probably within the one building. Fulling involved washing surplus oils from wool and pounding the cloth to produce a felted effect; sheep-rearing played an important role in the local economy. By 1695 it had reverted to being a corn mill. The mill closed at an unknown date in the early 19th century. A small, stone dwelling, probably 18th century, forms part of the present Mill Farmhouse. It has no rear windows so may indicate converted use of the old building or the former mill may have been adjacent, replaced by the newer section of the house.

The cultivation of crops was central to the feudal system of agriculture. Larger settlements usually had a system of three open-fields, smaller communities one or two. An open field at Wigwig is mentioned in 1262 (its precise location is unknown) and suggests that the hamlet has never been much greater in size than it is today. In the 13th century, assarting (clearing woodland for enclosure and settlement) was reported at Wigwig.

We start to find some interesting detail in the 16th century. In 1545, after the Dissolution, there was a sale by the Crown of the farm at Wigwig held in tenancy by Joan Sprott, to George Tresham and Edmund Twynyho. Some forty years later, by 1584, it was back in the Sprott family, now owned by one Richard Sprott, possibly Joan's son or grandson. In 1624 it was known as The Pall. Over a period from 1692-1706, most of the estate was bought by William Icke of Leegomery, later becoming Mill Farm.

In the same year, 1545, Tresham and Twynyho also purchased the farm held by Thomas Taylor. It shortly became part of the Belswardine estate of Thomas Harnage (d. c1562) The Harnages' estate grew over the centuries and by 1808 included Red House Farm, New House Farm and Homer Farm. Settlement in Wigwig followed a common Shropshire pattern, with farmhouses forming a central nucleus, surrounded by their fields. With names changing over time it is difficult to identify the present buildings with historical references. In 1670 the main house was Wigwig Hall (or Farm). The confined valley site of Mill farm, which would have been prone to flooding, seems unlikely to have been the preferred location of the main house. New House Farm was probably so named when rebuilt after a disastrous fire at the turn of the last century. Located high on a spur above Harley Brook, it may have been the site of the Medieval Hall but the adjacent Red House Farmhouse, with its complex structure and associated old barns and byres, is proposed as the strongest contender.

Red House Farm

Red House Farm is of great historical interest worthy of further investigation by an architectural historian. There may have been continuous settlement on the site for over a thousand years and incorporated into its fabric are ancient beams, stone and brick, suggesting at least three major periods of development.

An Edward 1 coin has been unearthed near the farmhouse, supporting an early foundation[xiii]. If this was the site of Elmar's Anglo-Saxon house, it would have been a timber-framed dwelling, Homer Wood providing an abundance of good oak. The oldest end-section of the present farmhouse consists of a long, narrow building, the far end of which has been used as a barn and undergone many changes. One of the most notable features at the front is an external staircase leading to two upper rooms, below which is an old, covered well colour photo 11.2, (centre section).

Near the top of the stairs is a small, early window and a 15th or possibly 14th century cusped brace[xiv] has been exposed below plaster. In the larger of the upper rooms and the gable end of the barn area above may be relic cruck[xv] timbers, pointing to a medieval farmhouse.[xvi]

There was a period of relative prosperity for agriculture, from around 1570 to 1640 when farmhouses were 'improved' or rebuilt.[xvii] This could involve entirely encasing a timber-framed house in brick, or brick-nogging (replacing old wattle and daub infill with brick). There appear to have been such improvements here in the seventeenth century, with brick-nogging using long, narrow bricks in a dark clay, lain as 'stretchers'. These same bricks can also be seen in the set of four, splendid chimneys set in the clay-tiled roof at the end of the central section of the building, colour photo 11.3, (centre section).

Some large blocks of Kenley Grit are revealed in the back wall, probably built as a stone chimney-breast for these, or earlier chimneys. Adjoining this area is the later bread-oven in Wenlock Limestone. The well-crafted rafters in the upper barn room of the end section are also probably 17th century.

The rear wall of the farmhouse is clad in another type of old brick, with a possible former doorway near the bread-oven, colour photo 11.4, (centre section).

The modern farmhouse kitchen area in this central section has low ceilings. It can be seen from the photographs how the roof line has been raised by several courses and a window infilled by a third type of larger and softer brick. The central portion of wall on the other side of the house has been completely clad in this brick, an improvement carried out during the final phase of development with the addition of a fine new wing and main entrance, of three bays and two and a half storeys, built some time in the 18th century at right angles to the original dwelling. It can be inferred from ceiling heights and the presence of four chimneys but only two remaining fire-places, that the earlier farmhouse extended beyond its present line, colour photos 11.3 & 11.4, (centre section). The old chimneys appear to have been shortened, perhaps to prevent their being visible above the roof-line of the new wing. Timber structures suggest the substantial weather-boarded barn facing this wing may have been part of the 17th century expansion, updated when the 18th century wing was added.

Homer

The two earlier references from the Much Wenlock Parish Registers of the mid 16th century show that a few cottages had begun to appear as the nucleus of the community of Homer. In a survey of royal woods and forests within Salop taken in 1556, there is mention of the common wood called 'Homer', a mature woodland of sixty years' growth, 'but the inhabitaunts wold be lothe to have the same sold, having no tymber else where for to repair their houses.'[xviii] The 17th century sees a trend of fairly rapid expansion of unlicensed, or 'squatter' dwellings on Homer common (still mainly wooded and, indeed, known as Homer Wood at that time), probably due to expansion in farming and early limestone quarrying nearby. In 1636 there were three cottages, which quadrupled to twelve by 1671. More appeared a few years later, in 1675, when it was recorded that new 'inclosures' were being made by recent settlers, of whom the writer had a poor opinion, describing them as 'extravagent and idle persons,' some of them strangers, traditionally held to be 'gypsies'. These figures refer to dwellings on Homer Common but there may have been several other cottages closer to the modern centre of the village. One of these is the original Homer Farmhouse, (1405, figure 11.1) now no longer inhabited and the only obviously timber-framed house in the village, colour photo 11.5, (centre section).
It is of box-framed construction,[xix] with one gable-end wall of stone and probably 17th century in date. It has a central chimney and at one time had a well close to the central front door. Lawrence's Cottage (1427, figure 11.1) is the village's sole remaining example of a thatched cottage, colour photo 11.6, (centre section).
Built of Wenlock limestone, it has an inglenook fireplace with bread oven and rough-hewn ceiling timbers with the bark left on. Its well, also close to the original front door, still survives. With no local supply of slate or other easily cleaved stone suitable for roofing, straw thatching seems likely to have been the most common roofing material until local clay tiles replaced it as affording durability and a lower fire risk.
By 1708, Homer had grown to a loosely scattered settlement of twenty-three cottages. An old stone cottage on Homer Hill (1502, figure 11.1) was one of only a handful of houses built in Homer during the 18th century. It is one of the few in the village that bear a date plaque, 1783. This period of population stabilization lasted into the mid-19th century, as

by the time of the first detailed Census Return of 1841, the village only comprised twenty-eight dwellings (see later section).

Roads, Track-ways and Paths

The ford at Wigwig has probably been a crossing point of the Harley Brook for over a millennium, the roadway below Red House and New House Farms being a classic example of a 'sunken lane'. The winding nature of the lane linking Wigwig and Homer, following old field boundaries, suggests a long-established route to Much Wenlock, climbing steeply up the hill and eroding through the centuries into another sunken lane. An alternative route from Wigwig to Wenlock, called the Church Way, is now no more than a neglected Public Footpath (figure 11.1) across the fields to join a side lane in Homer leading across Vineyard Road and on towards Homer Common to join the main road up the hill.[XX] Vineyard Road was the start of another, probably older, route to Wenlock, marked on the Tithe Map of 1847, continuing today as a popular Public Right of Way onto the Edge through Homer Head Coppice as a sunken lane, through a field called The Pretty Road joining the main road at the edge of town.

Much Wenlock would have been visited regularly with produce and animals for market and to buy goods. It had an amazing number of alehouses, twenty-one in 1614, and interestingly, Homer had two in 1681.[XXi] There is a long tradition of many families owning donkeys in Homer (indeed, it was known locally as 'Donkeyland'), perhaps dating back to settlement on the Common by 'gypsies'. The donkey-cart was still in use into the 20th century to transport people and goods up the steep hill to Wenlock and beyond.

A walk around Homer today reveals an extensive network of minor lanes and footpaths which grew up organically in response to needs: to connect families and as routes to work (figure 11.1). A path led through the lands of Homer Farm to Sheinton Mill and shortcuts from the village could be taken to the Wigwig mill. The network of lanes at the eastern end of the settlement linked the 'squatter' cottages on Homer Common and incorporated tracks to the local limestone quarries on Wenlock Edge. One of the hidden delights of Homer is 'The Steps', a long flight of over ninety substantial steps built to assist the climb up the very steep valley side and leading, along an obvious trackway, to the Sheinton road and thence to Gleedon and Tomlinson's quarries, colour photo 11.7, (centre section).

Great care was taken in construction, each step of large, hard bricks being edged with iron and backed by a ceramic drainage channel, colour photo 11.8, (centre section).

The Steps are actually across the parish boundary in Sheinton Parish and do not appear on the Tithe Map of 1847, but their location is marked on Map 2.

Squatter cottages were sited where opportunity arose but others were built for proximity to place of work, for the availability of a water supply and reasonably level land. Homer can be said to be a *spring-line* village, where shallow wells could be sunk, as at Lawrence's Cottage. There were also communal wells, one in Slade Lane, others elsewhere on Homer Common.[XXii] By the later 19th century, the settlement had expanded westwards along the main road through the village, and near the old route up Vineyard Road, the dwellings linked by a further network of lanes. The focus of the settlement had now shifted to this area and Homer's school was built at the junction of these two roads.

The Tithe Map and Apportionment

A key source for 19th century settlement is the Tithe Map and Apportionment. After an Act of 1836, parishes were allowed to change the age-old tithe payments (originally one tenth of income and usually paid in produce) to a rent charge, which entailed detailed mapping of the land. The 1847 Tithe Map for the Wenlock area[xxiii] gives a visual image of Homer and Wigwig at that date, as plots, houses and fields are marked, each with a number which relates to the *Apportionment* (figure 11.1). This comprehensive list records land ownership and land-use, and the occupier of each dwelling. In the 1980s H D G Foxall drew a series of maps for Shropshire matching the Tithe Map numbers to the field-names given in the Apportionment, thus giving us access to often centuries of local history, even back to the middle ages.

Homer

Map 2 is based on Foxall's map, on which land-ownership in Homer and Wigwig has been plotted from the Apportionment data. An interesting pattern emerges, with the land divided between three landowners (apart from two small, individually owned fields). The residents of Homer Township would have paid rent to The Right Honourable Lord Forester. At that time there were 34 loosely scattered households in Homer. Beside each cottage was normally a small garden for growing vegetables to supply the needs of the family and many of the tenants also rented a 'croft' (small enclosure)[xxiv] or meadow. Map 2 shows the close pattern of small plots around the cottages in contrast to the much larger fields of the surrounding farmland. Homer has long been associated with damsons. In 1847 around one third of the tenants had orchards, damsons and apples providing fresh fruit in the diet and supplementing the family income. The landowner was responsible for the maintaining roads and common land, such as the roads and wastes at Homer Common (1490) and another surviving patch of common (1490).

Homer Farm (1405), a small farm of around 40 acres, was owned by Sir George Harnage and occupied in 1847 by Edward Griffiths (colour photo 11.5). Most of its land lay in a block beyond the farmhouse, with two fields as a separate block to the west (figure 11.1). Both Homer and the three Wigwig farms practised the mixed husbandry of arable with pasture characteristic of the area. Land beside the brook provided good meadow grassland, and meadows were also found on poorly drained ground, as the field-name Withy Meadow (1399) suggests. The Apportionment lists oats as the main arable crop by volume in bushels, followed by barley and wheat. The landowner often kept for his own use areas of woodland as with Unshell Coppice (1374) and the Coppice in Withy Meadow (1400). Edward Griffiths also rented some land from Lord Forester, including a house near the site of Homer House (1457).[xxv] This house, along with stable and croft, were sublet to Joseph Edwards and also included a garden, orchard and three meadows. The fields called Spout Yard (332a), The Meadow (332c), and Omberslee (332e), shaded grey on Map 2, were part of Wenlock Township, owned by Sir Watkin Williams Wynne and occupied by William Reynolds. Two fields were owned by individuals, John Reynolds owning a small field to the south-west of Spout Yard (1409) and Elizabeth Rowe a meadow nearby (1393). Although the Tithe Map marks a building, probably a barn, in Spout Yard on the site of present day Bache Farm, it must be assumed that the house dates from a slightly later period, as there is no mention of a dwelling in the Tithe Apportionment.

Wigwig

Sir George Harnage also owned New House Farm in Wigwig (1345). Colour Photo 11.1, (centre section) shows that its land then extended from the edge of Homer Township to the Harley Parish boundary, separated into two blocks by the fields of Red House Farm. It was occupied by Richard Jones and his family. Again, the landowner kept the Coppice (1365) for his own use. Some particularly interesting field-names are found here. The Hair Chester (1351) and Upper Hair Chester (1352) have already been mentioned in connection with their proximity to the Roman villa site of Yarchester. 'Leasow' comes from the Old English word for 'pasture.' Fishpool Leasow (1334) may date back to when Wigwig was part of the Wenlock Priory estates; fish were commonly stocked in natural or purpose-built ponds for the table. The adjacent field, The Flax Piece (1336), suggests that flax-growing for linen was once practised. These two fields have unusually shaped southern boundaries and may be relics of Wigwig's medieval Open Field.

The adjacent Red House Farm (the largest at 104 acres) was owned in 1847 by the Reverend Samuel Minton, Vicar of Much Wenlock but occupied by Thomas Rudd and family. Its fields were the most dispersed although over the years there have been considerable boundary changes and today it incorporates the land of New House Farm.

Mill Farm's land (about 80 acres) extended along the narrow valley of the Harley Brook and across towards the edge of Homer Township. Meadowland bordered the brook, with arable on the more open fields. One of the meadows is called The Slang (1379), usually denoting a narrow piece of land beside a river, as in this case, or road. The old mill leat runs along the top boundary of this field. Figure 11.1 shows the farmyard situated across the brook from the mill-house, where the land was more suitable. Wenlock Parish boundary forms the western edge of Mill Farm, enclosing within it the strange anomaly of Mittand Pool Leasow (312 and 313). These two fields were owned by the Duke of Cleveland and not included in the Apportionment for Wigwig. Mill Farm was owned by William Icke of Belswardine Hall but occupied by Thomas Jarvis and his family.

Gleedon and Whitwell

Gleedon Hill Farm, part of Wenlock Township (as opposed to Wigwig and Homer Township), was owned by Francis Benthall and occupied by Jonathan Aston. It had a segmented pattern of fields, with a group below the farmhouse each side of the Sheinton road. Whitwell Cottage is absent from the Tithe Map but a cottage at Whitwell, within Wenlock Parish, is mentioned in the 1841 Census. A second group of fields was located to the west of the Homer road. Francis Benthall himself managed that part of Whitwell Coppice within Wenlock Parish and the extensive Homer Head Coppice, the semi-ancient woodland stretching along the upper slopes of Wenlock Edge and forming a natural boundary to Wigwig and Homer Township.

Jonathan Aston also rented land from Sir Watkin Williams Wynne in the area between the top of the Homer and Sheinton roads. He rented two arable fields on Tomlinson's Hill, site of one of the local limestone quarries. Although a building is marked beside the Wenlock road on the Tithe Map, it was probably a shed or barn, as 'Windmill Cottage' does not appear in the Census Returns until 1861.

The Schoolhouse
Centrally situated in the village, at the junction of the main street and Vineyard Road, Homer's school, built in local Wenlock limestone, still exists as a private house (figure 11.2).

Figure 11.2 (below), Homer School awaiting renovation in 2006 (D S Revell)

It was a 'voluntary' or 'Dame' school, dependent on income from local sources and Government grants for the payment of its teacher, building maintenance and the provision of equipment and materials for the scholars. Unusually, children as young as three commonly registered, attending until seven years of age (later eight) when they transferred to Much Wenlock School. Unfortunately, no registers have survived though two Log Books exist, covering the period 1874 to the school's closure in 1917, providing an insight into both the educational system of the time and the prevailing social and economic conditions. Some excellent plans for a 'Dame School' at Homer were drawn by the renowned Shrewsbury architect J Pountney-Smith in 1859, [xxvi] which suggests that it may well have opened as early as 1860. It was purpose-built, with the school-house an integral part (figure 11.3).

Figure 11.3, Homer School Plan, architect J Pountney-Smith, 1861 (courtesy of Much Wenlock Archives)

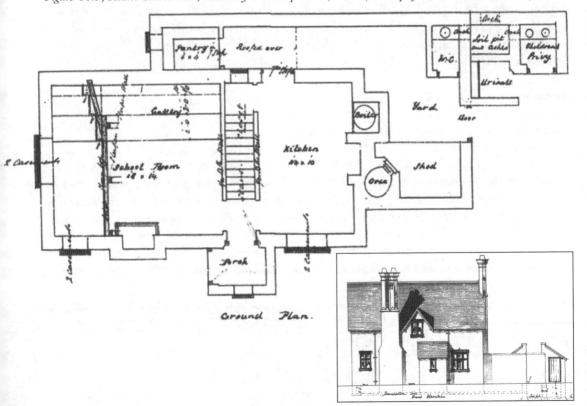

The schoolroom, approximately eighteen feet by fourteen, had two windows which on dull, winter days provided insufficient light for close work. It was heated by a single open fire, not lit until mid-October at the earliest.[xxvii] Along the length of the room were stepped 'galleries'. The front of the school, with its porched entrance, faced away from the main road, perhaps to allow the children access to their small play area; they were also allowed to play on the Common.[xxviii] The teacher's accommodation comprised a kitchen with pantry, and three bedrooms upstairs, two of them with fireplaces. Toilet facilities were separate from the main building and rudimentary – earth closets and urinals for the children and an adjoining but separate earth closet for the teacher.

Factors Affecting Attendance

There were usually fifteen to twenty-five children on the roll, though attendances fluctuated considerably. One of the main reasons was the frequency of serious epidemics, particularly Scarlet Fever, Diphtheria, Whooping Cough and Influenza. For example, in 1882 two children, Ellen Rowe and Sarah Rawlings died of Diphtheria and the Medical Officer of Health recommended the closure of the school for six weeks. Much time was lost in this way with serious implications for the teacher as a payment by results system operated. Severe winter weather also affected attendance. The Log Book records, on 8th January 1892, 'Deep snow – only ten children present & they were carried.' Although an Act of 1880 made attendance compulsory for children between five and ten, they were commonly absent when needed at home, to assist in looking after younger siblings if the mother was indisposed or to help with farming. On September 27th, 1904 the Mistress noted William Milner's absences. 'The boy himself says that his father required his services on the farm one day, and on the other day he was beating for the shooters.' Full advantage was taken of wild hedgerow fruits and flowers. When school re-opened after the Harvest holiday in 1890, only ten scholars appeared, 'the Blackberry gathering not finished.' On April 27th, 1891, there were, 'only 14 children present – the Coltsfoot season has commenced.' Coltsfoot leaves were used as a traditional remedy for coughs and as herbal tobacco.[xxix] The entry for May 16th, 1892 informs us that 'the cowslip gathering has commenced, some away for that purpose.' Cowslips were picked for sale and the making of wine.

School Life

The children probably welcomed the opportunity to take the odd day off from the limited and formal school curriculum. The aim of elementary education was then to provide moral training, basic literacy and numeracy, and, in Church schools, religious instruction. With no church in Homer, the Log Book records in 1884 that a Sunday School was held at the school and in 1895 that the school was used for evening services each winter Wednesday. The Mistress did her best in difficult circumstances, with woefully inadequate resources. In 1875 the annual Report of Her Majesty's Inspector stated: 'the instruction is moderately good. More books and Slates are needed, and a black-board, and form(s) and a colour box.' At this time, until rheumatism eventually forced her to resign in July 1888, Miss Susannah Hughes was the Mistress, a local girl, a Certified Teacher, Third Class. Although discipline and standards of attainment were often regarded by the Inspector as unsatisfactory,

Susannah was kind-hearted and the longest-serving teacher at Homer School. She was succeeded temporarily by a Miss Boden then by Miss Mary Jane Nicholas, a Certified First Class teacher, from April 1889 to October 1892, who did much to raise standards. After another temporary appointment of the unqualified Miss Rebecca Hopton for a few months, Miss Elizabeth Harling, a Certified teacher, First Class, was appointed in April 1893 until the end of April 1904 (figure 11.4).

Figure 11.4 Homer School 1904. Miss Harling and pupils (courtesy of Mr J McFall)

As Grants from the Education Department were a vital source of income, the annual Inspection was the most important event in the life of the school, when children would be examined in the *Three Rs* and Needlework. As payment by results continued until 1897, small schools like Homer were always at a disadvantage. The Curriculum gradually broadened in the last two decades of the 19th century to include 'Object lessons' and more practical activities, such as mat weaving and knitting.

Until 1891, when free education was introduced, School Pence, paid weekly by the children, were an important source of income. There is a noticeable increase in reporting of repairs to the fabric of the school after 1891. The fee was not standardised even within the local area. Non-payment was sometimes noted in the Log Book and a comparison between Much Wenlock School, which charged 6d per week from 1880, and Homer, which from 1876 onwards reduced its small fee further to 2d per week for the first child, 1d for the second and subsequent children from the same family, gives an insight into the struggle many families had to make ends meet[xxx]. Homer School was a Church of England foundation and the Vicars of Much Wenlock were Chairmen of the Managers. The Reverend and Mrs Ellis were frequent visitors from 1875 to the early twentieth century. Needlework was a compulsory subject and Mrs Ellis provided resources such as knitting needles and material for aprons. Lady Harnage in particular, along with a number of other local dignitaries such as Miss Seacome and Miss Furlong, provided generous and popular support and visited the school to hear the children sing, read and recite poetry. At the start of the autumn term and before Christmas, these visits often included a 'tea party' for the children and attendance was usually excellent on these days! On December 21st, 1882, 'Miss Seacome…presented all the children, 24 in number, with various kinds of Toys, and Scrapebooks, and those children which had attended School most regular and had paid their School pence, were presented with useful Articles of wearing apparral, also Biscuits, Ginger-bread and sweets, to all the children'. Lady Harnage presented a Bible to each child on its transfer to Wenlock School.

Homer School, through the latter half of the 19th century, was a focus of village life, supporting the local community and providing some basic literacy and numeracy skills for its young children close to home, before they continued their education in Much Wenlock.

THE CENSUS RETURNS
Population

The Census Returns from 1841 to 1901 are a key source for looking at change in a community. Collected every ten years, they are snapshots taken on a particular day in the life of that community. Although one has to be cautious when interpreting the data, they give an insight into the social and economic conditions of rural and urban dwellers in the 19th century. The Tithe Apportionment only stated the 'Occupier' of a cottage but the Census gives details of the entire household, and links can sometimes be made between a plot number and the 1841 and 1851 Censuses to locate families. The population in the Homer area peaked from 1861 to 1881, with a tailing off towards the end of the century (figure 11.5).

Figure 11.5 Homer Census 1841-1901 Population & number of houses

	Homer Hseholds.	Wigwig Hseholds.	Wh.-Gl. Hseholds.	Total Households.	Total Popn.	Avg. Hsehold Size.
1841	28	3	3	34	168	4.94
1851	29	3	4	36	160	4.44
1861	33	3	4	40	203	5.08
1871	36	3	5	44	209	4.75
1881	35	3	4	42	221	5.26
1891	35	3	2	40	184	4.60
1901	35	2	3	40	169	4.23

From 1861 the total number of households stayed relatively stable, with a peak of 44 in 1871, partly due to the start of a small inward migration of men of working age coinciding with a general increase in birth rate.

The 1891 and 1901 Censuses recorded the number of rooms occupied if fewer than five. In Homer that meant three-quarters of the cottages. The average household size was 4-5, but this includes households with elderly couples and masks the fact that many families had five or more children living in cramped conditions. For example, in 1891, Thomas Sankey, a 'stone quarry labourer,' lived with his wife Rosamond and six children between the ages of 6 and 29 in a four-roomed cottage in Homer. His two elder sons were also limestone quarrymen and the contribution of additional wage-earners must have made a significant difference to household income. It can be seen from colour photo 11.9, (centre section) that children and young people under twenty-one made up around half the population. Childhood epidemics, such as Diphtheria and Whooping Cough, took their toll, and caused fear in the community. The 'elderly'(over 60) made up a very small proportion of the population until about 1871 when life expectancy started to improve. Ages given in the census cannot always be relied upon but some people did manage to live to a good age. In 1851 William Hassal, a labourer from Homer, aged 75, was still working. With no State Welfare system, most men had to continue in work for as long as they were able, wages of agricultural and other manual labourers being too low to allow saving for old age. It fell upon the children to support their elderly parents when they were no longer able to live independently. The 1881 Census records Elisha Hill, born in Homer and aged 86, living with his daughter and son-in-law. And John Hughes, aged 85, lived with his daughter Susannah, the School Mistress, in the schoolhouse.

Population Mobility

The overwhelming majority of the Township population in the 19th century was born in Homer, Wenlock or within a twelve-mile radius. Colour photo 11.10 (centre section) shows the place of birth of the working-age population. In a rural-based economy, most were drawn from surrounding farms and villages, like Sheinton, Cound and Frodesley. There was considerable mobility within this local area as agricultural labourers were taken on by new employers at the hiring fairs. This makes the task of linking families to particular addresses very difficult. 1871 marked the start of a trend showing a small rise in people born further afield within Shropshire, in other English counties, Wales and Ireland. This is particularly noticeable in 1881, but actually only involved a few families and the township is characterised by very low mobility outside the immediate area. Being a rare event, one can imagine the interest aroused by the arrival of someone from Devon, Cumbria or Durham.

OCCUPATIONS
Agriculture

Around half the male working population was involved in agriculture, colour photo 11.11, (centre section)with a peak in 1861.[xxxi] The mid-19th century was a relatively prosperous period for British agriculture, with technological and scientific improvements enabling output to rise to meet the needs of a growing urban population, although the pace of change was slower on the small, mixed farms of this part of Shropshire.

It was followed by a long depression from the mid 1870s, when a series of poor harvests, and a rise in imports led to a sharp drop in farming income. Similarly, diseases in sheep and cattle, coupled with overseas competition, worsened the position of the agricultural labourer.[xxxii] But Figure 3 shows that the agricultural workforce was not reduced as much as might be expected,[xxxiii] perhaps a reflection of the land being estate-owned rather than owner-occupied. Male and female servants often 'lived in'. For example, in 1861 Clement

Downes, farmer of 100 acres in Wigwig, living with his wife and two children, is recorded as employing two men, a carter and an agricultural labourer, listed as part of the household along with a general servant.

The harvest was the focus of the farming year. Then, and at other peak times, seasonal labour would be required by the three Wigwig farms and Homer Farm, when farmers' and workers' wives and children 'pitched in', along with labour provided by the 'gypsy' community. Specific types of agricultural work are sometimes listed in the Census: William Sankey, in 1851, was a Molecatcher, who would have trapped a range of vermin; land drainers appear from the 1881 Census onwards (perhaps signifying more marginal land being brought into production or the introduction of new technology), as do men employed in Forestry, listed as 'woodsman' or 'sawyer.' It is unclear whether it had become more economic to manage the woodlands or whether these workers were previously incorporated with the 'agricultural labourers'.

Quarrying

Limestone quarrying was the other major occupation, at its peak employing around forty percent of the male labour force in 1841. The latter half of the 19th century saw a general decline in the industry but it was still important for Homer (fig 3), with local quarries at Gleedon, Tomlinson's Hill, the Sytche, Standhill and Shadwell. Men are described in the Census as 'rock labourer' or 'stone quarryman,' and occasionally 'lime burners'(who processed the limestone for fertiliser or flux for the iron industry). George Sankey of Homer was foreman at Standhill quarry[xxxiv] in 1880, which had a workforce of seven or eight quarrymen[xxxv]. He is described in the 1881 Census as a 'limestone rock manager,' and as a 'lime quarry foreman' in 1901, so had a position of considerable responsibility. Although there is no documentary evidence of commercial quarrying at Standhill or Shadwell before the 19th century, it is likely that small-scale working took place in earlier centuries, as on many of the quarry sites around Wenlock.

Tomlinson's Hill, on the eastern side of the area of land between the Homer and Sheinton road junctions with the Wenlock road, shows extensive evidence of old workings, now reclaimed by nature. The name probably originates from a William Tomlins of Homer, who acquired a 'parcel of limerocks' known as Stone Acre in 1745. He was granted freedom to burn and carry away limestone for a half-year rental of 15/-, on condition that he built a substantial house of stone or brick, with two rooms up and two down, by the following Michaelmas.[xxxvi] This was probably the cottage on the Wenlock road to the west of the quarry site, demolished in the 1960s and now replaced by a new stone house. Several cottages are mentioned, but un-named, in the Census data for the Gleedon area. A 'Windmill Cottage' is specified in 1861, 1881, 1891 and 1901 which, given its location, may well be this dwelling. Some years later, John Tomlins, probably the son of William, 'took a limerock in Homerfield' in the holding of Elizabeth Tomlin and paid the Wynnstay Estate 4d per ton for the extracted stone.

There is an early reference to quarrying at Gleedon Hill in the 16th century when a Glebe of the Vicar of Much Wenlock included a profitable stone quarry on Gleedon Hillfield.[xxxvii] Extraction at Gleedon Quarry appears to have wound down in the latter half of the century and it had closed by 1901. A similar situation applied at Tomlinson's.

Other Occupations

There is an interesting fluctuation through the 19th century Censuses in the proportion of males employed in other occupations, ranging from around 10% in 1841 to around 30% in 1881, mainly a function of the state of agriculture and quarrying. A key local event, the building and opening of the railway from Much Wenlock to link with the Severn Valley Railway at Buildwas in 1862, is reflected in the employment of three Homer men as railway labourers in 1861; platelayers are listed in later years. There is mention of carpenter, blacksmith and forgeman and in the later Censuses we start to see commercial occupations such as a fish and poultry dealer, butcher, grocer, and merchant's clerk.

In the earlier Census years, boys, sometimes as young as 10, were employed as domestic servants. This was the main occupation of girls on leaving school and women who remained unmarried, along with related positions such as housekeeper or charwoman. In general, married women stayed at home to bring up the children, although many would have been involved in seasonal agricultural work. Home-based occupations included dress-maker and laundress who were generally widows or unmarried women living with parents or siblings and needing to contribute to the household income. The School Mistress was the only 'professional' in the village, and probably had a rather lonely position, not fitting in socially with the parents of her scholars or the local dignitaries who came to visit.

CONCLUSION

An investigation of primary and secondary historical sources has led to some understanding of how the local community developed.

REFERENCES AND NOTES

i   Bowcock, E W, *Shropshire Place Names,* Wilder, Shrewsbury, 1923, p252

ii Gelling, M, in collaboration with Foxall, H D G, *The Place-names of Shropshire, Part One,* EPNS, 1990, p315.

iii Gelling, M, paper in *Medieval Archaeology, Vol XI,* 1967, pp87–104

iv Hill, T G, *The Possible Significance of the Wardine and Wic Place-names in Shropshire,* Paper submitted to the TSAHS (to be published 2006)

v   SA Tithe Apportionments, microfilm no 147

vi *Domesday Book,* fol 258

vii Currie, C R J, *The Victoria County History, Shropshire, Vol XI,* OUP, 1998, p413 and *passim*

viii Gelling, M, in collaboration with Foxall, H D G, *The Place-names of Shropshire, Part Three,* E P N S, 2001, p270

ix Hartshorne, Revd C H, *Extracts from the Register of Sir Thomas Butler, Vicar of Much Wenlock, in Shropshire,* Tenby, 1861, pp7 & 15

x   Mills, A D *A Dictionary of English Place-Names,* incorporated in *The Oxford Names Companion,* OUP, 2002, pp301, 302

xi *Domesday Survey,* Fol 258

xii A villein had the highest status among unfree tenants who owed services and rents to the lord of the manor for their share of the land; bordar – a smallholder on the next rung down; serfs at the bottom holding no land.

xiii Oral information from Tom and Graham Clark. The present whereabouts of the coin are unknown.

xiv   A piece of curved timber set diagonally against a vertical and horizontal beam designed to prevent distortion of a framework and sometimes used decoratively

xv   A pair of inclined timbers, usually wrought from a single tree, forming an arch. Moran, M, *Vernacular Buildings of Shropshire,* Logaston Press, 2003, p540

xvi   Grateful thanks go to Madge Moran, architectural historian, for her analysis of photographs of the farmhouse and suggestions regarding interpretation of phases of development.

xvii   Garner, L, *The Buildings of Shropshire, Vol 11: The Tudor and Stuart Legacy,* Swan Hill, 1989, p1

xviii   Page, W A, (ed), *VCH Shropshire, Vol 1,* Constable, London, 1908, p492

xix   Moran, M, *op cit* p81, states that the term is used for a timber-framed building not of cruck construction. The method allowed more internal space and flexibility of construction, or alteration, of existing buildings.

xx   Wigwig residents attended both Much Wenlock and Harley churches.

xxi   *op cit* p413. These alehouses were part of the family home rather than separate establishments.

xxii   Marked on the 1:2500 O. S. map of 1884.

xxiii   Tithe map, Township of Wigwig and Homer, 1847, SA PF 198/4/1

xxiv   *Field, J A, History of English Field-Names,* Longman, 1993, p20. A 'croft' was often associated with a cottage and represented a plot which could sustain a family's subsistence needs.

xxv   It has to be noted that Foxall's maps are not always strictly accurate regarding the plotting of cottages.

xxvi   Wenlock Archives

xxvii   Coal came from Madeley Wood Colliery, sometimes bought more cheaply at the pit-head and carried by donkey cart by the children's fathers. McFall, J, *Education in the Rural Area of Much Wenlock, Shropshire, in Relation to Developments in National Education, 1870-1902,* Dissertation, University of Keele, 1970, p44

xxviii   *ibid,* p54, conversation with Mr E W Hill

xxix   Mabey, R, 'Flora Britannica,' Sinclair-Stevenson, 1996, p377

xxx   Homer School Log Book, 4.12.1886

xxxi   The data for 1871 has been omitted as it is unsatisfactory.

xxxii   Hill, R, & Stamper, P, *The Working Countryside 1862-1945,* 1993, pp10-11.

xxxiii   In 1871: 21,165 labourers, 6102 farmers in Shropshire; in 1911 13,497 and 5543 respectively. *Ibid,* p13

xxxiv   Shadwell Quarry was adjacent to Shadwell, on the Wenlock side.

xxxv   Williams, J Glynn, *The Wenlock Limestone Industry,* 1997, p106

xxxvi   *ibid,* p116, from *Wenlock Estate Book* (Sir Watkin Williams Wynn), 1785

xxxvii   National Library of Wales, Wynnstay box 56/110

ILLUSTRATIONS

COLOUR PHOTOGRAPHS,

CENTRAL SECTION